Sing, Spell, Read & Write®

36 Steps to Independent Reading Ability
Assessment Book

17 Book End Assessments for Phonetic Storybooks and 2 Achievement Tests

Teacher's Annotated Edition

Sue Dickson

MODERN CURRICULUM PRESS
Pearson Learning Group

Table of Contents

Book End Assessments

Achievement Tests

Name _____ Date _____

Book End Assessment for
Phonetic Storybook 1

Short a words

STUDENT ASSESSMENT RECORD			
RACEWAY STEP 6	Number Possible	Number Correct	Percentage of Mastery Score
Word Recognition	20	_____ × 5 =	_____ %
Word Comprehension	20	_____ × 5 =	_____ %
Picture-Word Matching (Word Recognition and Comprehension)	20	_____ × 5 =	_____ %
Story Comprehension	10	_____ × 10 =	_____ %
Missing Letters	10	_____ × 10 =	_____ %

Total Mastery Score

Sum of _____ % ÷ 5 _____ %

Word Recognition and Comprehension

1.	2.	3.	4.	5.
cat	(tag)	<u>pal</u>	Val	cap
(can)	<u>Dad</u>	(at)	<u>wax</u>	(and)
<u>bat</u>	hat	a	(Dan)	<u>glad</u>

6.	7.	8.	9.	10.
<u>Sam</u>	(van)	(pass)	and	<u>ham</u>
(map)	mat	<u>nap</u>	<u>bag</u>	(the)
tan	<u>pan</u>	grab	(had)	man

11.	12.	13.	14.	15.
can	<u>jam</u>	(man)	sad	<u>fast</u>
<u>wag</u>	(rag)	bag	(Max)	(last)
(fat)	has	<u>bad</u>	<u>sand</u>	has

16.	17.	18.	19.	20.
<u>ran</u>	tap	<u>raft</u>	<u>pat</u>	(Pam)
sat	<u>scat</u>	(ham)	(had)	nap
(Hal)	(lap)	past	crab	<u>gas</u>

Word Recognition [   ]
Number Correct

Word Comprehension [   ]
Number Correct

Picture-Word Matching

Name _____

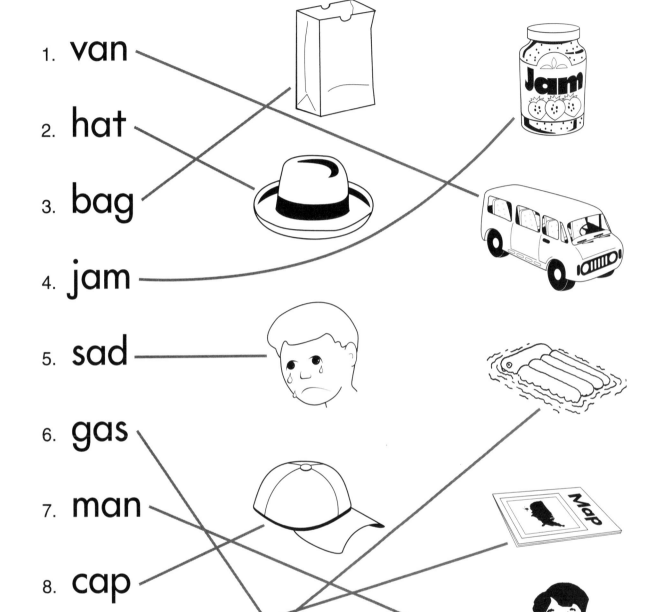

1. van

2. hat

3. bag

4. jam

5. sad

6. gas

7. man

8. cap

9. map

10. raft

Go on ▶

Word Recognition and Comprehension:
Storybook 1 Assessment, page 2

Picture-Word Matching

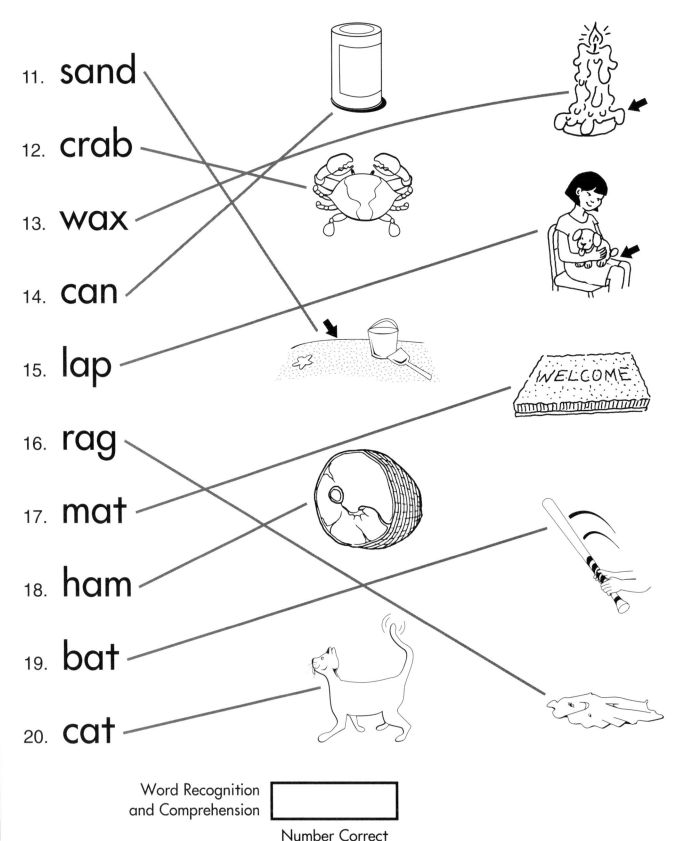

11. sand

12. crab

13. wax

14. can

15. lap

16. rag

17. mat

18. ham

19. bat

20. cat

Word Recognition and Comprehension

[   ]

Number Correct

Word Recognition and Comprehension:
Storybook 1 Assessment, page 3

Story Comprehension

Name _____

1. Val has a cap.

2. Dad has a van.

3. A man has a gas can.

4. The van has Val,
   Hal, Max, and the bag.

5. Max has the cap!

Go on ➤

Story Comprehension:
Storybook 1 Assessment, page 4

Story Comprehension

6. A man had ham and jam.

7. Max can tap Hal.

8. Hal ran past a crab.
   Max ran past a crab.

9. Hal and Max nap at last!

10. Val has Hal.
    Dad has Max.

Story Comprehension

Number Correct

Story Comprehension:
Storybook 1 Assessment, page 5

Missing Letters

Name _____

1. ra_g	2. pa_n	3. ha_t
4. _cat	5. s_and	6. r_aft
7. _ham	8. _map	9. _nap
10. b_ag		

Missing Letters [ ]

Number Correct

Name _____ Date _____

Book End Assessment for
Phonetic Storybook 2

Short e words

STUDENT ASSESSMENT RECORD				
RACEWAY STEP 8	**Number Possible**	**Number Correct**	**Percentage of Mastery Score**	
Word Recognition	20	_____ × 5 =	_____ %	
Word Comprehension	20	_____ × 5 =	_____ %	
Picture-Word Matching (Word Recognition and Comprehension)	20	_____ × 5 =	_____ %	
Story Comprehension	10	_____ × 10 =	_____ %	**Total Mastery Score**
Missing Letters	10	_____ × 10 =	_____ %	
		Sum of _____ % ÷ 5	_____ %	

Sing, Spell, Read & Write.

Word Recognition and Comprehension

1. (ten) wet get	**2.** fell red (pet)	**3.** hen (pen) fed	**4.** jet (red) peck	**5.** mess (best) left
6. (eggs) Ken mess	**7.** (next) peck pen	**8.** help mend (held)	**9.** (bent) Tess yells	**10.** (end) Jeff red
11. fell held (yells)	**12.** bent (nest) next	**13.** Tess (get) gets	**14.** went (help) next	**15.** hen (went) eggs
16. rest (yes) end	**17.** Peg fell (yet)	**18.** mend (left) went	**19.** wet Peg (let)	**20.** nest (mess) west

Word Recognition [ ] Number Correct

Word Comprehension [ ] Number Correct

© Pearson Education, Inc./Modern Curriculum Press/Pearson Learning Group. All rights reserved. Copying strictly prohibited.

14

Word Recognition and Comprehension:
Storybook 2 Assessment, page 1

Picture-Word Matching

Name _____

1. pet
2. best
3. yells
4. fell
5. mess
6. bent
7. mend
8. hen
9. end
10. peck

Go on →

Word Recognition and Comprehension:
Storybook 2 Assessment, page 2

15

Picture-Word Matching

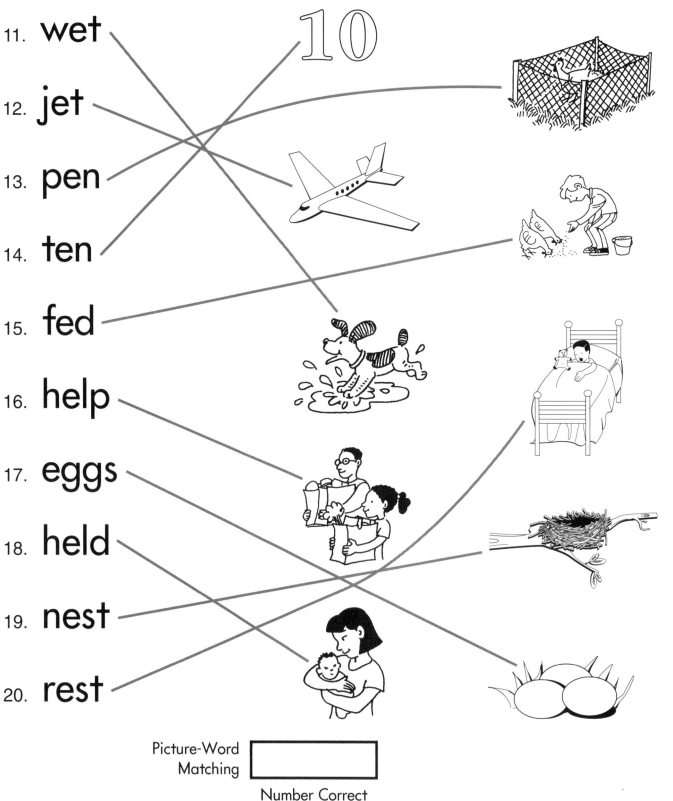

11. wet

12. jet

13. pen

14. ten

15. fed

16. help

17. eggs

18. held

19. nest

20. rest

Picture-Word
Matching

Number Correct

Word Recognition and Comprehension:
Storybook 2 Assessment, page 3

Story Comprehension

Name _____

1. The nest has ten eggs.
   The nest has ten tan eggs.

2. Jeff has a pet hen.
   Jeff has Tess.

3. Jeff yells, "Nan, help!"
   Jeff tells Nan, "Tess has
   a bent pen."

4. Tess can peck and
   peck and peck.

5. Nan can mend
   the bent pen.

Go on ➡

Story Comprehension

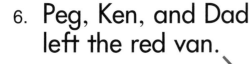

6. Peg, Ken, and Dad
   left the red van.

7. The bag fell.
   Dad has a mess.

8. Dad gets ham
   and eggs.

9. The red jet left.
   The red jet went fast.
   The red jet went west.

10. Peg and Ken can rest
    at last.

Story
Comprehension

Number Correct

18

Story Comprehension:
Storybook 2 Assessment, page 5

Missing Letters

Name _____

1. b ent	2. ten t	3. j et
4. h en	5. w et	6. e ggs
7. n e st	8. m e nd	9. p e ck
10. pe n		

Story
Comprehension

Number Correct

Name _____ Date _____

Book End Assessment for
Phonetic Storybook 3

Short **i** words

STUDENT ASSESSMENT RECORD

RACEWAY STEP 10	Number Possible	Number Correct	Percentage of Mastery Score	
Word Recognition	20	_____ × 5 =	_____ %	
Word Comprehension	20	_____ × 5 =	_____ %	
Picture-Word Matching (Word Recognition and Comprehension)	20	_____ × 5 =	_____ %	
Story Comprehension	10	_____ × 10 =	_____ %	**Total Mastery Score**
Missing Letters	10	_____ × 10 =	_____ %	

Sum of _____ % ÷ 5 _____ %

21

Word Recognition and Comprehension

1. is (in) it	2. yip bit (miss)	3. (it) Bill bit	4. six slip (Sis)	5. dip (Jim) did
6. as (is) big	7. grins (wins) Tim	8. rim hit (quick)	9. Ripp (his) it	10. (him) hit rim
11. dip his (did)	12. will (bit) quick	13. mitt (spin) win	14. Jill (win) will	15. (Liz) miss grins
16. Sis him (big)	17. (will) wins win	18. slip (tip) mitt	19. (Tim) spin Jim	20. (hit) his in

Word Recognition [ ] Number Correct

Word Comprehension [ ] Number Correct

Word Recognition and Comprehension:
Storybook 3 Assessment, page 1

Picture-Word Matching

Name _____

1. in

2. slip

3. miss

4. him

5. big

6. fill

7. mitt

8. tip

9. gift

10. dig

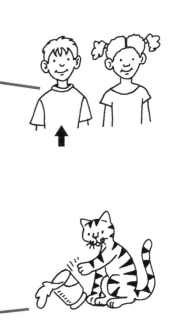

Go on

Word Recognition and Comprehension:
Storybook 3 Assessment, page 2

Picture-Word Matching

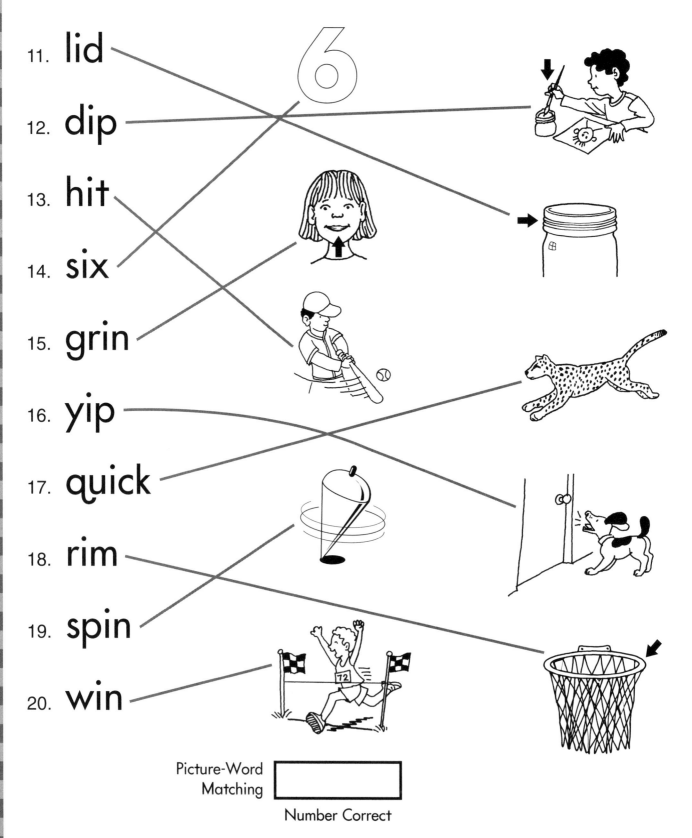

11. lid

12. dip

13. hit

14. six

15. grin

16. yip

17. quick

18. rim

19. spin

20. win

Picture-Word Matching | Number Correct

Word Recognition and Comprehension:
Storybook 3 Assessment, page 3

Story Comprehension

Name _____

1. Dad will help Jim bat.

2. Jim has a mitt.

3. Jim can hit well.
   "Yip, yip," went Ripp!

4. Dad can bat well.
   Dad can hit!

5. Dad can tell Jim is big.

Story Comprehension

6. Jill can lift it.
   Can Jill get it in?

7. Liz has it. Liz is fast.
   Can Liz get it in?

8. Liz is quick. Liz gets it. ——————— 1

9. Liz wins. Bill and Tim clap.

 2

10. Liz can dip past Jill.

 3

Story
Comprehension

Number Correct

Story Comprehension:
Storybook 3 Assessment, page 5

Missing Letters

Name _____

1. m_i_tt	2. si_x_	3. _y_ip
4. _h_it	5. _d_ip	6. m_i_ss
7. sli_p_	8. spi_n_	9. _r_im
10. gr_i_n		

Missing Letters [ ]

Number Correct

Name _____ Date _____

Book End Assessment for Phonetic Storybook 4

Short o words

STUDENT ASSESSMENT RECORD

RACEWAY STEP 12	Number Possible	Number Correct	Percentage of Mastery Score	
Word Recognition	20	_____ × 5 =	_____%	
Word Comprehension	20	_____ × 5 =	_____%	
Picture-Word Matching (Word Recognition and Comprehension)	20	_____ × 5 =	_____%	
Story Comprehension	10	_____ × 10 =	_____%	Total Mastery Score
Missing Letters	10	_____ × 10 =	_____%	
		Sum of _____% ÷ 5	_____%	

Sing, Spell, Read & Write.

Word Recognition and Comprehension

1. on / top / (Spot)	**2.** fox / (box) / fog	**3.** pot / hop / (dot)	**4.** dots / got / (log)	**5.** (doll) / fog / jog
6. Mom / stop / (plop)	**7.** not / pot / (was)	**8.** (hop) / stop / log	**9.** (jog) / fog / from	**10.** box / (lot) / Tom
11. (Todd) / clock / pom-pom	**12.** (on) / lot / top	**13.** log / (socks) / blocks	**14.** (not) / fog / frog	**15.** plop / clock / (rock)
16. (to) / on / doll	**17.** plop / Spot / (stop)	**18.** rock / not / (Ron)	**19.** fox / (top) / box	**20.** socks / (blocks) / pot

Word Recognition [ ] Number Correct

Word Comprehension [ ] Number Correct

30 Word Recognition and Comprehension:
Storybook 4 Assessment, page 1

Picture-Word Matching

Name _____

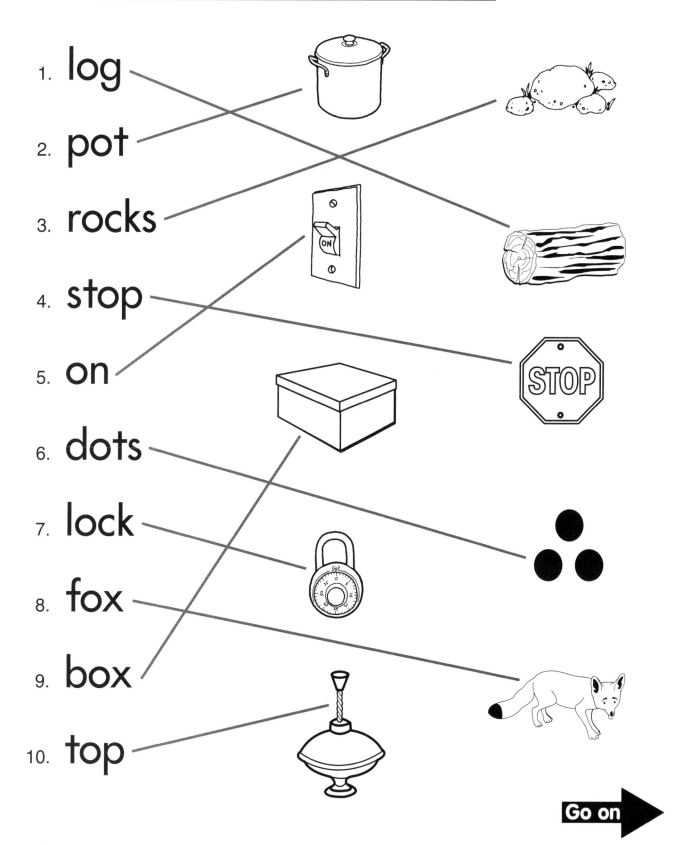

1. log
2. pot
3. rocks
4. stop
5. on
6. dots
7. lock
8. fox
9. box
10. top

Go on

Word Recognition and Comprehension:
Storybook 4 Assessment, page 2

Picture-Word Matching

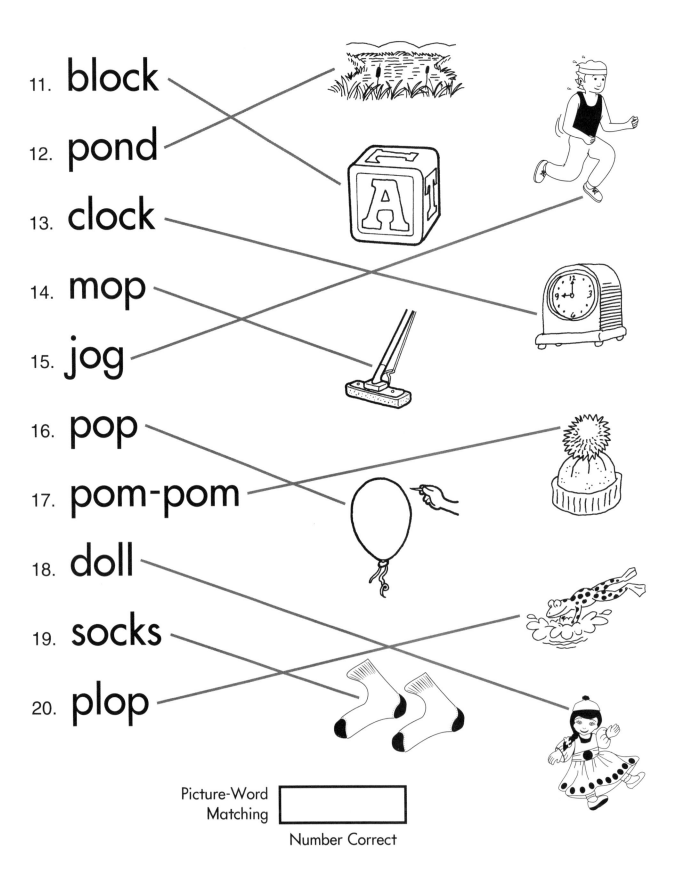

11. block

12. pond

13. clock

14. mop

15. jog

16. pop

17. pom-pom

18. doll

19. socks

20. plop

Picture-Word
Matching
Number Correct

32 **Word Recognition and Comprehension:**
Storybook 4 Assessment, page 3

Story Comprehension

Name _____

1. At last, Ron got to the pond.
   The fog was bad.

2. The clock said six.
   Ron got his socks.

3. Ron Fox had a quick
   jog with Tom Frog.

4. Plop! Tom Frog sat
   on a rock next to Ron.

Go on ➡

Story Comprehension

5. Jill set Kim on the bed.

6. Spot hid Kim in the big pot.

7. Jill went to get Kim.
   Kim was not on the bed!

8. Spot got the doll from the pot.

1

9. Jill ran to Todd. Kim is
   not on the bed.

2

10. Todd did not have Kim.

3

Story
Comprehension

Number Correct

Missing Letters

Name _____

1. p o t	**2.** fro g	**3.** p o nd
4. r ocks	**5.** d o ll	**6.** l og
7. cl o ck	**8.** s ocks	**9.** bo x
10. f ox		

Missing Letters [ ]

Number Correct

Name _____ Date _____

Book End Assessment for
Phonetic Storybook 5

Short u words

STUDENT ASSESSMENT RECORD

RACEWAY STEP 14	Number Possible	Number Correct	Percentage of Mastery Score	
Word Recognition	20	_____ × 5 =	_____ %	
Word Comprehension	20	_____ × 5 =	_____ %	
Picture-Word Matching (Word Recognition and Comprehension)	20	_____ × 5 =	_____ %	
Story Comprehension	10	_____ × 10 =	_____ %	Total Mastery Score
Missing Letters	10	_____ × 10 =	_____ %	

Sum of _____ % ÷ 5 _____ %

Word Recognition and Comprehension

1. pup ⟨rubs⟩ mud	2. ⟨bug⟩ rug tub	3. bus Gus ⟨cup⟩	4. hum ⟨hug⟩ but	5. ⟨fun⟩ dug cut
6. up ⟨us⟩ but	7. bud ⟨bun⟩ fun	8. cup cups ⟨tug⟩	9. rug Mutt ⟨pup⟩	10. ⟨run⟩ bud Judd
11. fuzz drum ⟨snug⟩	12. ⟨dug⟩ bug bun	13. ⟨hut⟩ stuck gum	14. fun mud ⟨nut⟩	15. cups dust ⟨us⟩
16. ⟨truck⟩ umbrella jump	17. dull tub ⟨cut⟩	18. ⟨hum⟩ just snug	19. ⟨must⟩ puff dust	20. ⟨puff⟩ bus fuzz

Word Recognition [ ] Number Correct

Word Comprehension [ ] Number Correct

Word Recognition and Comprehension:
Storybook 5 Assessment, page 1

Picture-Word Matching

Name _____

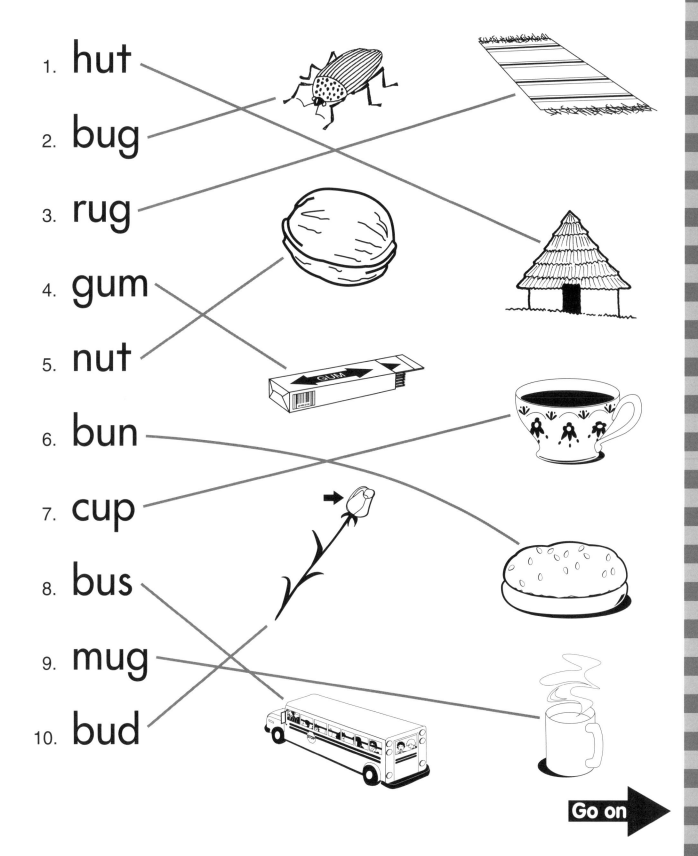

1. hut
2. bug
3. rug
4. gum
5. nut
6. bun
7. cup
8. bus
9. mug
10. bud

Go on ➡

Word Recognition and Comprehension:
Storybook 5 Assessment, page 2

Picture-Word Matching

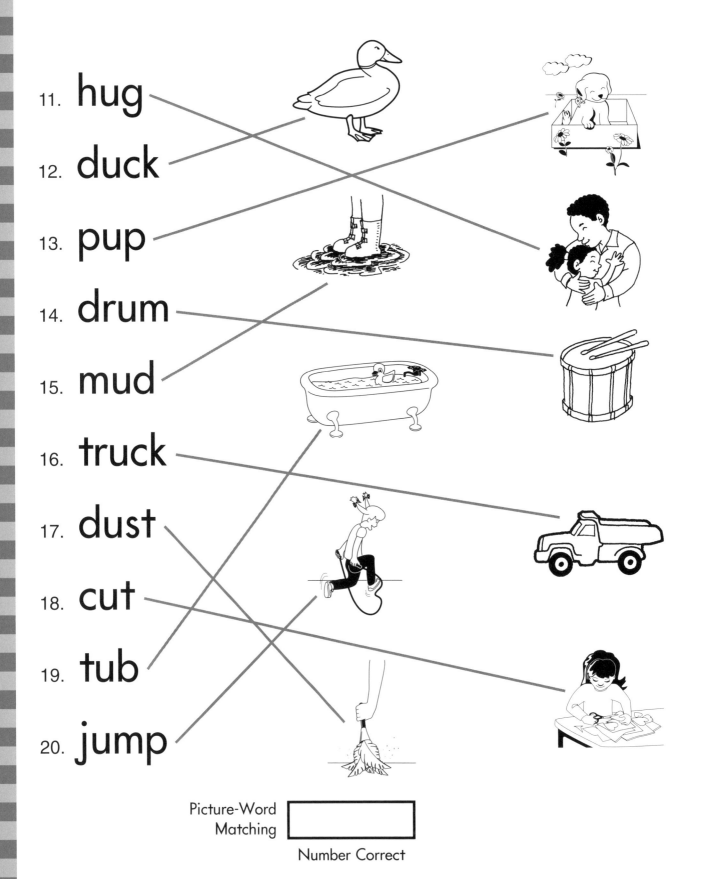

11. hug

12. duck

13. pup

14. drum

15. mud

16. truck

17. dust

18. cut

19. tub

20. jump

Picture-Word Matching

Number Correct

Word Recognition and Comprehension:
Storybook 5 Assessment, page 3

Story Comprehension

Name _____

1. Next, Gus has fun in the mud.
   Gus dug and dug.

2. Gus and his mom and his dad
   have a hut. It is a nut.

3. Gus has ham on
   a bun. It is a big bun.
   Mom will cut the bun.

4. Gus has a truck and a bus.
   Gus has fun in the truck.

5. Gus has an umbrella.
   Will Gus get wet?

Go on ➜

Story Comprehension

6. Gus and Judd can swim in the cup. Judd can jump up and in.

7. Judd will help Gus tug.

8. Rub-a-dub-dub! Dad rubs a bug in a tub.

9. Gus is snug in his bed.

10. Dad will fill the tub.

Story Comprehension

Number Correct

Story Comprehension:
Storybook 5 Assessment, page 5

Missing Letters

Name _____

1. tu b	2. b u g	3. r ug
4. p u p	5. m ud	6. b u n
7. n u t	8. bu s	9. hu g
10. c ups		

Missing Letters [ ]

Number Correct

Name _____ Date _____

Book End Assessment for
Phonetic Storybook 6

Short vowels

STUDENT ASSESSMENT RECORD

RACEWAY STEP 15	Number Possible	Number Correct	Percentage of Mastery Score	
Word Recognition	20	_____ × 5 =	_____ %	
Word Comprehension	20	_____ × 5 =	_____ %	
Sentence Comprehension	20	_____ × 5 =	_____ %	**Total Mastery Score**
Story Comprehension	5	_____ × 20 =	_____ %	
		Sum of	_____ % ÷ 4 _____ %	

Sing, Spell, Read & Write.

Word Recognition and Comprehension

1. (lumps) lamp lip	2. stick (spill) sled	3. sits (steps) sock	4. lift (lock) neck	5. flag flaps (flop)
6. runs (jumps) rests	7. (hill) hog hot	8. Ted tack (kids)	9. Rick (rust) desk	10. hands bump (hand)
11. (grand) brick bell	12. bin (bend) band	13. trip strum (swam)	14. (black) block back	15. fix fills (fist)
16. stiff stamp (sift)	17. (mix) mop men	18. pin (pick) pest	19. digs (dock) dent	20. (vest) wig wind

Word Recognition [ ]
Number Correct

Word Comprehension [ ]
Number Correct

Sentence Comprehension

Name _____

1. The man hit his fist on the rug.

2. "I have a rust rug," said the man.

3. Mom went to get a rug.

4. "It has the best back," said the man.

Go on ➤

Sentence Comprehension

5. Ted gets gas in his truck.

6. The red truck went past a bell. The red truck went past a well.

7. It went past a frog, and a log, and a hog.

8. It went past a top and a mop.

Go on

Sentence Comprehension:
Storybook 6 Assessment, page 3

Sentence Comprehension

Name _____

9. Dad will set the desk on the rug.

10. Mom will set the lamp on the rug.

11. Dad can lift the rug if Mom, Tim, and Meg help.

12. Dad will tack the rug.

Go on ➤

Sentence Comprehension

13. Bill went to camp.

14. "I will jump back into the pond."

15. Bump! Bump! Bill swam into Rob, but it was not a bad bump.

16. Rob sits and rests with Bill.

Go on ➡

Sentence Comprehension

Name _____

17. The cup fell.
Pat had a spill!

18. Pat has milk on her lip, her neck, and her leg.

19. Mom will help Pat.
Mom will fix a wet lip.

20. Pat gets ham and milk.

Sentence
Comprehension

Number Correct

Story Comprehension

Don has a drum.
Bob can strum.
Gwen can hum.
Rick will tap.
Rick has a band.
"A band is a lot of fun," said Rick.

1. _____ had a band.

Don	Gwen	Rick	Bob
○	○	●	○

2. Rick is _____.

glad	sad	mad	bad
●	○	○	○

3. How many are in the band?

5	4	3	30
○	●	○	○

4. This story is about a _____.

class	band	picnic	hat
○	●	○	○

5. Gwen can _____.

sing	clap	tap	hum
○	○	○	●

Story
Comprehension
[   ]
Number Correct

Assessment

Raceway Steps 19-20

Name _____ Date _____

Book End Assessment for
Phonetic Storybook 7

Sight words; words with two vowels:
ea, ee, ai, oa, ie; silent e̸; c = s

STUDENT ASSESSMENT RECORD

RACEWAY STEPS 19–20	Number Possible	Number Correct	Percentage of Mastery Score	
Word Recognition	20	_____ × 5 =	_____ %	
Word Comprehension	20	_____ × 5 =	_____ %	
Sentence Comprehension	25	_____ × 4 =	_____ %	**Total Mastery Score**
Story Comprehension	10	_____ × 10 =	_____ %	
		Sum of	_____ % ÷ 4	_____ %

Sing, Spell, Read & Write

Word Recognition and Comprehension

1. <u>beach</u> (beans) east	**2.** (cream) <u>clean</u> came	**3.** lace <u>leap</u> (lean)	**4.** (team) teach <u>tea</u>	**5.** <u>slice</u> (space) spice
6. <u>seats</u> meat (year)	**7.** <u>bake</u> bite (bike)	**8.** feel (feed) <u>feet</u>	**9.** <u>smile</u> (mile) pile	**10.** <u>heat</u> (hear) ear
11. <u>home</u> (come) cone	**12.** cried (tree) <u>three</u>	**13.** (need) <u>green</u> creep	**14.** make <u>rake</u> (wave)	**15.** pie <u>price</u> (peach)
16. <u>soak</u> float (boat)	**17.** (snail) <u>trail</u> sail	**18.** trace (twice) <u>time</u>	**19.** <u>race</u> (rice) rode	**20.** (chase) <u>shade</u> made

Word Recognition [   ] Number Correct

Word Comprehension [   ] Number Correct

54

Word Recognition and Comprehension:
 Storybook 7 Assessment, page 1

Sentence Comprehension

Name _____

1. "I like nuts," said Tom. Mom said, "We can buy two bags."

2. Mom said to Tom, "Would you get the eggs?"

3. "May I get one apple for me, one for Jim, and one for Tom?" asked Linda.

4. Mom said to Jim, "See if you can get the bananas."

Go on →

Sentence Comprehension

5. "See Dad float. Dad can float on his back!" said Mom.

6. "I see some seaweed," said Sis.

7. "See us do a leapfrog," said Jack.

8. Dad will get the umbrella and the beach seats.

Go on ➤

Sentence Comprehension

Name _____

9. "Come with me, Sis," said Jack. "We can sail the sailboat."

10. "We can have our picnic," said Mom.

11. "I will set up the beach umbrella," said Dad.

12. "It is very hot," Mom said. "We will go to the beach."

Go on ➤

13. Dad likes to bake. Dad will make the cake for Dan.

14. "Yes, you may go on a hike with Jake," said Dad.

15. "Would you like to go on a hike, Mike?" asked Jake.

16. "We will be back on time," said Mike.

Go on ➤

Sentence Comprehension

Name _____

17. "Let's get Dave to the vet."

18. Gail has three rabbits. Her rabbits are Duke, Dave, and Zeke.

19. The vet could feel the bump on Dave's nose.

20. A bee was near Dave. The bee bit Dave on his nose.

Go on ➤

Sentence Comprehension:
Storybook 7 Assessment, page 6

59

Sentence Comprehension

21. Grace has a happy face. She likes to help. She will clean the rug.

22. Joe and Grace had a race to dust and wax.

23. "Mom likes this lace one," said Grace. "Help me place it on the table, Joe."

24. "Mmmm," said Grace. "That ham with spice smells nice, Mom."

25. "Here, you can help Dad dice the carrots," said Mom.

Sentence Comprehension [ ]

Number Correct

Sentence Comprehension:
Storybook 7 Assessment, page 7

60

Story Comprehension

Name _____

"Come here, Tom," said Mom. "Come here, Jim and Linda!"

"We will all go to Sal's," she said. "We will buy some ham, milk, and eggs. We can buy some snacks."

"We do not have very many apples," said Jim. "We love apples. May we get some?" he asked.

"Yes, we will buy some apples and bananas," said Mom.

1. Why will Mom go to Hal's?

   ○ to see Jim, Tom, and Linda

   ● to buy ham, milk, eggs, and snacks

   ○ to get some beans

   ○ to buy wax

2. _____ went to Hal's.

   ○ Mom, Dan, Tim, and Linda

   ○ Bill, Dad, Jack, and Pam

   ○ Peg, Pam, Tom, and Dick

   ● Mom, Jim, Tom, and Linda

Go on ➜

Story Comprehension

Look back at the story if you need help.

3. Can Mom buy a dress at Hal's?

    Yes   No
    ○   ●

4. Jim, Tom, and Linda are _____.

    sad   mad   bad   glad
    ○   ○   ○   ●

5. This story is about _____.

    ○ a trip to camp
    ● a trip to Hal's
    ○ two apples
    ○ Mom has ham

Go on

Story Comprehension

Name _____

Just then Vince came home. He held a nest in his hand.

"Mom, Dad, see what I have!" he said.

"That is nice, Vince," said Mom, "but you must place it back in the tree."

Vince was back fast. "Let me help you," he said. "What can I do?"

"You are nice, Vince," said Mom. "Ask Dad if he can use your help."

"You can buy the ice cream," said Dad.

6. Vince had a _____ in his hand.

    ham   net   nest   jet
    ○   ○   ●   ○

7. When must Vince place the nest back in the tree?

    five o'clock   now   soon   six o'clock
    ○   ●   ○   ○

Go on

Story Comprehension

Look back at the story if you need help.

8. What did Vince ask Mom?
   - ○ May I go?
   - ○ Will Dave come?
   - ● What can I do?
   - ○ What will we eat?

9. What will Vince do for Dad?
   - ○ bake a cake
   - ● buy the ice cream
   - ○ make the ham
   - ○ get green beans

10. Could this story happen?

     Yes   No
      ●   ○

Story
Comprehension
Number Correct

Name _____ Date _____

Book End Assessment for
Phonetic Storybook 8

āy̸; y = ī; g = j; y = ē; Suffixes **ed, er, ing**

STUDENT ASSESSMENT RECORD

RACEWAY STEP 21	Number Possible	Number Correct	Percentage of Mastery Score	
Word Recognition	20	_____ × 5 =	_____ %	
Word Comprehension	20	_____ × 5 =	_____ %	
Sentence Comprehension	25	_____ × 4 =	_____ %	**Total Mastery Score**
Story Comprehension	10	_____ × 10 =	_____ %	
		Sum of	_____ % ÷ 4	_____ %

Word Recognition and Comprehension

1. (pay) stay play	2. bay (day) hay	3. way (jay) pay	4. (clay) play lay	5. say (Ray) May
6. baby (funny) silly	7. stay (today) away	8. berry (pretty) windy	9. (shy) sky why	10. pay (pry) cry
11. why dry (try)	12. jogged (jumped) jumping	13. huffing (puffing) packed	14. baked mailed (waved)	15. (painting) picking playing
16. drumming drummer (dumped)	17. giraffe (huge) bulge	18. hiked (honked) hopped	19. (driver) jogger painter	20. locking (looking) hopping

Word Recognition [ ]
Number Correct

Word Comprehension [ ]
Number Correct

Word Recognition and Comprehension:
Storybook 8 Assessment, page 1

Sentence Comprehension

Name _____

1. "Look!" yelled Kenny. "I see a man picking up a rock."

2. A man was fixing his tire. The tire was flat.

3. They could see a red truck as it dumped sand.

4. "I see two hikers who have hiked up a steep hill," yelled Kenny.

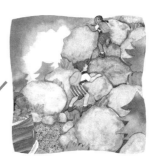

5. "I see a truck driver who is waving at us," said Dad.

Go on ➤

Sentence Comprehension

6. "I will make a clay blue jay.
   I will name my blue jay Kay."

7. "Good-bye, little Fay!"
   "Good-bye, blue jay!"

8. On a nice hot day in May,
   Fay went to see her pal Ray.

9. The blue jay came fast at little Fay.
   "Stay away. Please stay away!"
   said the jay.

10. Fay was glad that day. On her
    way, she did see a tree with a
    big blue jay.

Go on ▶

Sentence Comprehension

Name _____

11. A little fly came by. "Why do you cry, Giraffe?" asked the fly.

12. "You just pry up the **sh** from **shy.**"

13. "Yes, I will try," said the huge giraffe. "I will pry up the **sh** and set in the **tr.**"

14. "I did it!" This made the huge giraffe bulge with pride!

15. A huge giraffe sat crying and crying and crying.

Go on ▶

Sentence Comprehension

16. "It is time to go. Wave good-bye to Freddy, Billy, and Gary."

17. "It must be windy to fly a kite. Look up at the flag! See? No wind, or the flag would wave!"

18. Freddy had his kite in his hand. He was really upset.

19. "Have a berry to eat," said Lucy. "Thank you Lucy," said Billy and Gary.

20. "Here, Sally, have a berry," said Lucy.

Go on ➡

Sentence Comprehension

Name _____

21. "I see a lady who is mailing a letter," said Mom.

22. "I see a painter painting an ad!" yelled Kenny.

23. "I see a baseball game! A batter has hit the ball and is running to first base."

24. Patty and Kenny raced to the van. Mom got in humming a happy tune.

25. A bunny was hopping by the road.

Sentence Comprehension ☐

Number Correct

Story Comprehension

Lucy likes to baby-sit for Sally. Sally is happy. She has a pretty baby doll.

"Here, Sally, have a berry," said Lucy. "Would you like a red berry, a purple berry, or a black berry?"

"I like red berries," said Sally.

1. Sally has a _____.

    pup   dot   cat   doll
     ○   ○   ○   ●

2. What is Lucy doing?
   - ○ She is playing.
   - ● She is baby-sitting.
   - ○ She is sleeping.
   - ○ She is crying.

Go on

Story Comprehension:
Storybook 8 Assessment, page 7

Story Comprehension

Name _____

Look back at the story if you need help.

3. Who is Lucy baby-sitting?
   ○ Freddy
   ○ Billy
   ○ Sandy
   ● Sally

4. Lucy gave Sally some _____.
   ○ apples
   ● berries
   ○ bananas
   ○ buns

5. Did Sally like the berries?

   Yes   No
   ●   ○

Go on ▶

"We would like to go see Jimmy and Penny Kane. May we, Daddy?"

Dad said, "Yes, let's go see the Kanes!"

Patty and Kenny jumped up. "That will be fun!"

"You can go and get packed," said Mom. "We will leave at sunrise on Friday."

6. How did Patty and Kenny feel when Dad said they could go see the Kanes?

glad	sad	safe	silly
●	○	○	○

7. What did Patty and Kenny do?
   ○ They baked a pie.
   ○ They went for a hike.
   ○ They sat on a mat.
   ● They jumped up.

Go on

Name _____

Look back at the story if you need help.

8. What did Mom tell Patty and Kenny to do?

pack	play	bake	eat
●	○	○	○

9. When will they leave?

○ at one o'clock

○ at ten o'clock

● at sunrise

○ at sunset

10. Could this story happen?

Yes	No
●	○

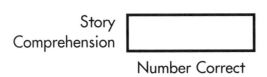

Story Comprehension [   ]

Number Correct

Name _____   Date _____

Book End Assessment for
Phonetic Storybook 9

or, sh, ch, er, ir, ur

STUDENT ASSESSMENT RECORD

RACEWAY STEPS 22A–D	Number Possible	Number Correct	Percentage of Mastery Score	
Word Recognition	20	_____ × 5 =	_____ %	
Word Comprehension	20	_____ × 5 =	_____ %	
Sentence Comprehension	20	_____ × 5 =	_____ %	**Total Mastery Score**
Story Comprehension	10	_____ × 10 =	_____ %	
			Sum of _____ % ÷ 4 _____ %	

1. (fort) torn forks	**2.** (sort) pork sore	**3.** north (order) sport	**4.** stork store (short)	**5.** core corn (for)
6. (rush) hush wish	**7.** (bench) bunch lunch	**8.** porch (scorch) orchard	**9.** march (munch) ranch	**10.** cheese (cherry) child
11. shin (shine) shirt	**12.** burst (crush) crash	**13.** inch each (reach)	**14.** (better) fisher over	**15.** fir stir (dirt)
16. chirp (cheer) chain	**17.** (skirt) hurt hurry	**18.** chest (chip) chose	**19.** (curb) hurt hurry	**20.** firm germ (turn)

Word Recognition [ ] Number Correct

Word Comprehension [ ] Number Correct

Word Recognition and Comprehension:
Storybook 9 Assessment, page 1

Sentence Comprehension

Name _____

1. "I see a box," yelled Kate. "It has a big stork on it." "Here is a big apple box," said Kevin.

2. At last, Kevin and Kate go home! They gave Mom her order.

3. "You may go to the store," said Mom. "You can pick up my order. It is on this list."

4. See Kevin and Kate's fort! What fun they will have!

Go on ➜

Sentence Comprehension

5. "I will name my hot rod Red Flash. I will be a champ with Red Flash," said Chet.

6. "See me dip the brush in the can?" said Dad. "I am careful to press it on each side so the paint will not drip."

7. "I need my chisel to chip off one inch from this end," said Dad. "The chisel is in the chest."

8. "I can do it," said Chet. "It is fun! I will not spill or drip the paint."

Go on ➡

Sentence Comprehension:
Storybook 9 Assessment, page 3

Sentence Comprehension

Name _____

9. "Third, we will turn it over and lift up the pail," said Miranda.

10. "Look," said Ervin. "I see a bird. Did you hear it chirp in the fir tree?"

11. "First, we must fill up my purple pail with dirt and stir it," said Miranda.

12. "I like chocolate dirt," said Ervin, "but Mom's lunch is better! I'll race you inside, Miranda!"

Go on →

Sentence Comprehension:
Storybook 9 Assessment, page 4

Sentence Comprehension

13. At two o'clock, the chimes ring. Then, the children race to the beach at the pond.

14. The children eat lunch in the ranch hut. They sit on a bench. Not one inch of the bench is left to sit on!

15. The children go for a swim. It is safe to swim when you have a buddy.

16. Each day the children go to the chicken pen to help feed the chickens.

Go on ➡

Sentence Comprehension

Name _____

17. Sheldon left his bike by the side of the driveway. He hopped up the path and held his shin.

18. Sheldon giggled. Mom was glad to see him happy once more.

19. "Did you crush your hand?" asked Mom.

20. "What did you do?" asked Sheldon's mom.
"I fell off my bike," said Sheldon.

Sentence Comprehension
☐
Number Correct

Story Comprehension

"I would like to make a hot rod," said Chet. "I would like to race it in the next Hot Rod Race."

"Fine," said Dad. "I will help you."

Each day Dad and Chet did more.

Dad said, "We need a chain. Can you can reach it, Chet?"

"Yes, Dad," said Chet.

"I need my chisel to chip off one inch from this end," said Dad. "The chisel is in the chest."

"Yes, here it is," said Chet.

1. What would Chet like to make?

   a hot rod   a box   a can   a hot dog

   ●   ○   ○   ○

2. Will Chet race his hot rod in the Hot Rod Race?

   Yes   No

   ●   ○

3. Did Chet and Dad make the hot rod in one day?

   Yes   No

   ○   ●

Go on ➡

Story Comprehension

Name _____

Look back if you need help.

4. Dad needed a _____ to chip off one inch.

   chain   paint   brush   chisel

    ○   ○   ○   ●

5. Where did Chet find the chisel?

   ○ on a shelf

   ○ in a box

   ● in the chest

   ○ in a can

Go on ➡

Story Comprehension

"Mom! The term is over! I am a third grader now!" yelled Jenny. "May we go to the seashore?" she asked.

"Yes, we can go next Thursday," said Mom.

"Yippee!" cried Jenny. "I will need new shorts and a shirt."

"OK," said Mom. "Let's go to Shirley's shop on Third Street."

Jenny and her mom went to Shirley's store to shop.

"I need a new skirt. You need shorts and a shirt. We need a clerk to help us," said Mom.

6. What grade is Jenny going to be in?

first	second	third	fourth
○	○	●	○

7. What does Jenny need for the seashore?
- ○ new shoes
- ● new shorts and a shirt
- ○ a bunch of socks
- ○ a blue skirt

Go on →

Story Comprehension:
Storybook 9 Assessment, page 9

Story Comprehension

Name _____

Look back if you need help.

8. Jenny was a _____ last term.

- ● second grader
- ○ first grader
- ○ fourth grader
- ○ third grader

9. Jenny and her mom will go to the store on
_____.

- ○ Church Street
- ● Third Street
- ○ Green Street
- ○ Cherry Street

10. Jenny will feel _____ when she gets
to the seashore.

   sad   mad   fussy   happy

   ○   ○   ○   ●

Story
Comprehension

[   ]

Number Correct

Name _____ Date _____

Book End Assessment for
Phonetic Storybook 10

th, tch, oor = or, ABC Code

STUDENT ASSESSMENT RECORD

RACEWAY STEP 23	Number Possible	Number Correct	Percentage of Mastery Score	
Word Recognition	20	_____ × 5 =	_____ %	
Word Comprehension	20	_____ × 5 =	_____ %	
Sentence Comprehension	20	_____ × 5 =	_____ %	**Total**
Story Comprehension	10	_____ × 10 =	_____ %	**Mastery Score**

Sum of _____ % ÷ 4 _____ %

Sing, Spell,
Read & Write.

Word Recognition and Comprehension

1.	2.	3.	4.	5.
(thin)	them	(thump)	think	(doors)
them	(these)	mother	things	floor
thick	things	Roth	(thick)	catch

6.	7.	8.	9.	10.
stretch	match	thin	these	patch
switch	(catch)	thump	(those)	(doing)
(Smith)	snatch	(thing)	both	speeding

11.	12.	13.	14.	15.
match	(crutches)	(mother)	(their)	Smith
(Mitch)	matches	with	reader	(both)
stitches	pitches	Theo	stories	with

16.	17.	18.	19.	20.
patch	watch	(switch)	pitcher	watch
pitch	(pitcher)	clutch	(pitches)	Butch
(pages)	catcher	snatch	Gretchen	(match)

Word Recognition [ ] Number Correct

Word Comprehension [ ] Number Correct

90 Word Recognition and Comprehension:
Storybook 10 Assessment, page 1

Sentence Comprehension

Name _____

1. "Look!" said Thad.
   "What is that thing?"
   "That is a cub!" said Mom. _____

2. What a thump! Thump! Thump!
   "It's the mother!"

3. "Look! Now there are three cubs."

4. All at once, the cub slipped and fell.
   The cub made a little thump.

Go on ➡

Sentence Comprehension

5. Such cheering and yelling there was! "Maybe we will win!" the Blue team cried.

6. "You are up, Kristy! Let 'em have it!" her team yelled. Kristy did!

7. The Red Team had their plans! "We can't let them beat us," they groaned. "Let's get going!"

8. The Red team had a problem. Their catcher was on crutches. He had stitches in his leg.

Go on

Sentence Comprehension

Name _____

9. Pam and Ann raced on their way to the store.

10. Pam and Ann waved to Mom. Then, they were off to the store.

11. Today is payday. Pam and Ann will get their pay from Mom.

12. Pam and Ann Smith like to help. They will make their beds.

Go on ➡

Sentence Comprehension

13. Mittens can stretch and bat the bag off the shed.

14. Mittens jumps on the bag. "You like this sport, Mittens," said Mitch.

15. Mitch kicks the bag. He can switch it from one leg to the other.

16. Mitch filled a bag with beans. Now he will stitch it up.

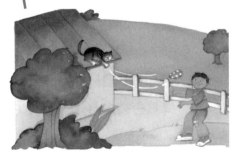

Go on ➡

Sentence Comprehension:
Storybook 10 Assessment, page 5

Sentence Comprehension

Name _____

17. There was Mr. Roth. "Hello, Mr. Roth," Ann said. "We came to get some fun things to eat."

18. Ann picked a box of nuts. "I would like one of these please," she said.

19. Pam said, "I think I will take two boxes of dried cherries and three apples, please."

20. Mr. Roth handed each girl her bag. "Thank you Mr. Roth," said the girls.

Sentence Comprehension [   ]

Number Correct

Sentence Comprehension:
Storybook 10 Assessment, page 6

Mitch filled a bag with beans. Now he will stitch it up.

Mitch kicks the bag. He can switch it from one leg to the other.

Mitch has a little cat. Mittens likes to watch Mitch play. She thinks this looks like fun!

Mitch can switch the bag to his feet. He can stretch his leg to kick the bag, but the bag lands on a patch of grass.

All at once, Mittens makes a dash to snatch the bag.

1. Mitch made a _____.

   box   mat   bean bag   mitt
   ○   ○   ●   ○

2. Mittens is Mitch's pet. Mittens is a
   _____.

   duck   pig   cat   dog
   ○   ○   ●   ○

Go on ➡

Story Comprehension:
Storybook 10 Assessment, page 7

Story Comprehension

Name _____

Look back if you need help.

3. Mittens likes to _____.

   ○ sleep on a mat

   ○ jump on the bed

   ● watch Mitch play

   ○ nap on Mitch's lap

4. To play the game, Mitch kicks the bag with his legs or his _____.

   bat   hands   feet   stick

   ○   ○   ●   ○

5. This story is about _____.

   ○ a baseball game

   ○ a bike ride

   ● a game Mitch and his cat play

   ○ a trip to the store

Story Comprehension

By the time you read this story, your Raceway car is speeding on the Language Arts Raceway to Step 24! Why are you doing this? So you will be a good reader.

When you know the ABC Code, you can use it to unlock words and read stories that tell about all sorts of things.

With the ABC Code, you can read anything you want. You can open doors to anyplace and anything. Those doors are the covers of books!

6. What is the next Step after you read this?

Step 21   Step 20   Step 32   Step 24
   ○   ○   ○   ●

7. Why are you going on the Language Arts Raceway?

   ● so you will be a good reader

   ○ to play a game

   ○ to sing a song

   ○ to race cars

Story Comprehension

Name _____

Look back if you need help.

8. You will like to _____ when you know the ABC Code.

play	skate	read	cry
○	○	●	○

9. In the story it said, "You can open doors to anyplace and anything." This means _____.

   ○ you can use a map

   ○ you can unlock a door

   ● you can read about anyplace and anything in books

   ○ you can play

10. This story is about _____.

playing	singing	reading	jumping
○	○	●	○

Story Comprehension

☐ Number Correct

Name _____   Date _____

Book End Assessment for
Phonetic Storybook 11

ow, ou, ōw, ew, qu, wh

STUDENT ASSESSMENT RECORD

RACEWAY STEPS 24A–C	Number Possible	Number Correct	Percentage of Mastery Score	
Word Recognition	20	_____ × 5 =	_____ %	
Word Comprehension	20	_____ × 5 =	_____ %	
Sentence Comprehension	25	_____ × 4 =	_____ %	**Total Mastery Score**
Story Comprehension	10	_____ × 10 =	_____ %	
		Sum of _____ % ÷ 4	_____ %	

Sing, Spell, Read & Write®

Word Recognition and Comprehension

1. found (loud) sounds	2. (towel) town cow	3. (hour) scouts owl	4. gown (clown) down	5. loud brown (house)
6. blows (show) frown	7. crow (grow) row	8. couch around (ground)	9. (howled) flower flour	10. (chow) howl bowed
11. (few) flew blew	12. snow (snowman) window	13. quit quite (quiz)	14. screws scouting (crew)	15. mew (Stewart) shower
16. queen (quick) quilt	17. wheat (where) which	18. (snowing) growing clowns	19. (scout) shouted shout	20. awhile quiet (question)

Word Recognition [   ]
Number Correct

Word Comprehension [   ]
Number Correct

Word Recognition and Comprehension:
Storybook 11 Assessment, page 1

102

Sentence Comprehension

Name _____

1. "Hi, Molly," said Cody. "Would you like to see me paint my face?"

2. One clown was in a funny gown, upside down!

3. Uncle Howard met Mom and Molly at the big tent.

4. There was a clown with a brown owl and a clown with a flower.

Go on →

Sentence Comprehension

5. Kara ran into the house. "Mom!" she shouted. "Look at this paper."

6. Mrs. Proud said, "Please come in."

7. Kara gave a loud shout. "Yippee!" she said. "I am going to be a Brownie Scout!"

8. Mrs. Proud began to tell Mom and Kara about scouting.

Go on ▶

Sentence Comprehension:
Storybook 11 Assessment, page 3

Sentence Comprehension

Name _____

9. "The north wind blows, and we have snow and a snowman!" said Dad from the window.

10. Owen, Karen, and Becky ran out to make a big snowman.

11. "Here is a carrot for a nose," said Becky. "Let's add a bow tie at the neck," said Karen.

12. "Look, Dad! We put stones in a row for buttons," said Becky.

Go on ➡

13. On his way to the pond, Drew met Newton, his big cat.

14. At last, the raft was finished. It even had a sail on the mast!

15. "Let's make a raft to sail on the pond," said Stewart.

16. "Look at the new crew!" yelled Drew.

17. All at once, lots of things happened! Newton jumped onto the raft.

Go on ▶

Sentence Comprehension

Name _____

18. Mom gave Nadia a big hug. "Thank you, Nadia," she said.

19. On Mother's Day, Nadia's surprise was finished. "A quilt!" Mom cried when she saw it.

20. "I must get the quilt finished on time," said Nadia to herself.

21. "What are you doing, Nadia? What are those little scraps of cloth?" Mom asked.

Go on

Sentence Comprehension

22. "Look at that sign," said Abby. "I can read it! W-h-i-s-k! Whisk Inn!"

23. "What is that growing over there?" asked Frank. "That is wheat," said Dad.

24. The Wheelers have a new white car. They are going on a day trip in it.

25. Dad will take the wheel and drive for awhile. Mom will look at the map.

Sentence Comprehension [ ]

Number Correct

Sentence Comprehension:
Storybook 11 Assessment, page 7

108

Story Comprehension

Name _____

Uncle Howard and Cody were pals.

"Hi, Molly," said Cody. "Would you like to see me paint my face?"

"Wow! Yes!" said Molly.

Cody the Clown put thick white cream on his face.

Then, he painted fat red lips. Next, he put a big pink spot on each cheek.

"Now, what is missing?" asked Cody with a frown.

"Your big red nose!" said Molly.

Cody put on his huge red nose and bowed to Molly. Molly just howled!

1. Cody and _____ were pals.

   Uncle Howard   Dad   Mom   Molly
      ●   ○   ○   ○

2. What did Cody put on <u>first</u>?

   ○ a big red nose

   ○ fat red lips

   ○ a big pink spot on each cheek

   ● thick white cream

Go on →

Story Comprehension

Look back if you need help.

3. After Cody put on his fat red lips, he put on

   _____.

   ○ thick white cream
   ● a big pink spot on each cheek
   ○ a big red nose
   ○ a big red hat

4. What was missing in the end?
   ○ a hat for Cody
   ○ Uncle Howard's ticket
   ● Cody's big red nose
   ○ the can of white cream

5. Did Molly like to see Cody put on his makeup?

        Yes   No

        ●   ○

Go on

Story Comprehension:
Storybook 11 Assessment, page 9

Story Comprehension

Name _____

When Nadia could hear her mom's quick steps come near, she would quit making the quilt.

"I must get this quilt finished on time," said Nadia to herself.

On Mother's Day, Nadia's surprise was finished.

"A quilt!" Mom cried when she saw it. "It is so pretty! This is quite a surprise. Even a queen would love this quilt, Nadia!"

Mom gave Nadia a big hug. "Thank you, Nadia," she said. "I will always see your love in each little stitch of that quilt! Thank you for a very happy Mother's Day!"

6. Nadia made a _____.

doll   book   quilt   cake
○   ○   ●   ○

7. She made it for _____.
   ○ her sister's birthday
   ● Mother's Day
   ○ her grandmother's birthday
   ○ her teacher's birthday

Go on →

Story Comprehension

Look back if you need help.

8. Why would Nadia quit when Mom came near?
   - ○ She was finished.
   - ● She wanted to surprise Mom.
   - ○ She did not do her job.
   - ○ It was time to stop.

9. How did Nadia make the quilt?
   - ○ She glued it.
   - ● She stitched it.
   - ○ She cut it.
   - ○ She washed it.

10. How did Mom show she liked the quilt?
    - ○ She sat up.
    - ○ She gave the quilt to Nadia.
    - ● She gave Nadia a hug and thanked Nadia.
    - ○ She put the quilt in a box.

Story Comprehension [ ]

Number Correct

Name _____ Date _____

Book End Assessment for
Phonetic Storybook 12

ar, aw, au, ing, ang, ong, ung, oy, oi

STUDENT ASSESSMENT RECORD

RACEWAY STEPS 25A–C	Number Possible	Number Correct	Percentage of Mastery Score	
Word Recognition Step 25A	20	_____ × 5 =	_____ %	
Word Comprehension Step 25A	20	_____ × 5 =	_____ %	
Word Recognition Step 25B	20	_____ × 5 =	_____ %	
Word Comprehension Step 25B	20	_____ × 5 =	_____ %	
Word Recognition Step 25C	20	_____ × 5 =	_____ %	
Word Comprehension Step 25C	20	_____ × 5 =	_____ %	
Sentence Comprehension	20	_____ × 5 =	_____ %	Total Mastery Score
Story Comprehension	10	_____ × 10 =	_____ %	
			Sum of _____ % ÷ 8 _____ %	

Sing, Spell, Read & Write

Word Recognition and Comprehension

1.	2.	3.	4.	5.
<u>hard</u>	(Mars)	<u>artist</u>	cart	stars
harmony	jars	darted	(cars)	<u>sparkle</u>
(harp)	<u>cars</u>	(smart)	<u>starts</u>	(large)

6.	7.	8.	9.	10.
Mars	arms	<u>darker</u>	(bark)	jars
<u>Carlos</u>	<u>jar</u>	darted	<u>park</u>	(dark)
(Martha)	(armful)	(Darby)	sharp	<u>yarn</u>

11.	12.	13.	14.	15.
<u>barked</u>	<u>farm</u>	(marble)	charm	jar
barn	starts	<u>Marla</u>	<u>arms</u>	(artist)
(cart)	(hard)	go-carts	(farm)	<u>stars</u>

16.	17.	18.	19.	20.
<u>large</u>	(yarn)	cars	<u>sharp</u>	harmony
mart	<u>barn</u>	(charm)	(starts)	<u>dark</u>
(starting)	barnyard	<u>Bart</u>	starting	(darker)

Word Recognition [ ] Number Correct

Word Comprehension [ ] Number Correct

Word Recognition and Comprehension:
Storybook 12 Assessment, page 1

Word Recognition and Comprehension

Name _____

1. (law) jaw autumn	**2.** lawn fawn (yawn)	**3.** jaw (hawk) paws

4. August applause (because)	**5.** straw Claude (paused)

6. crawling (fawn) Paul	**7.** (caw) law dawn	**8.** hawk claws (paws)

9. automobile (automatic) August	**10.** (flaw) jaw haul

11. fawn caw (straw)	**12.** flaw law (lawn)	**13.** (dawn) fawn yawn

14. gnawed (August) autumn	**15.** (haul) Claude crawling

16. paused (applause) automatic	**17.** yawn (automobile) because	**18.** claws (jaw) hawk

19. haul Paul (hauling)	**20.** (gnawed) paws flaw

Word Recognition
[ ] Number Correct

Word Comprehension
[ ] Number Correct

Word Recognition and Comprehension:
Storybook 12 Assessment, page 2

1. (sang) banged <u>rang</u>	2. <u>strong</u> (song) sing	3. <u>ring</u> king (wing)	4. hung <u>lungs</u> (rung)	5. (toy) <u>enjoy</u> boy
6. (enjoy) <u>royal</u> Joyce	7. boil (broil) <u>foil</u>	8. join (noise) <u>toy</u>	9. (stamping) watching <u>wishing</u>	10. <u>long</u> strong (lungs)
11. <u>king</u> toppling (long)	12. Troy <u>spoil</u> (coins)	13. <u>wing</u> Irving (everything)	14. <u>boil</u> broil (spoil)	15. strong (rung) sing
16. join <u>coins</u> (foil)	17. <u>boy</u> (Troy) noise	18. <u>Joyce</u> enjoy (royal)	19. (king) <u>kingdom</u> Ingrid	20. <u>spring</u> (singing) nothing

Word Recognition [   ]
Number Correct

Word Comprehension [   ]
Number Correct

116 **Word Recognition and Comprehension:**
Storybook 12 Assessment, page 3

Sentence Comprehension

Name _____

1. Dad had a large, sharp fork.
   He was lifting hay into a cart.

2. Bart dropped the hay by
   old Martha.
   "Arf, arf!" barked Sparkle.

3. This is Bart and this is
   Harmony Hill Farm.

4. "You can take this armful
   of hay over to Old Martha,"
   said Dad.

5. "Here, Sparkle," said Bart. "Let's
   go see Dad. He is in the barn."

Go on ➤

Sentence Comprehension:
Storybook 12 Assessment, page 4

117

Sentence Comprehension

6. At dawn, a fawn got up from its place, a sleepy look still on its face.

7. The fawn then saw the mouse run fast. It jumped in a hole as the hawk flew past.

8. The fawn munched green stems.

9. The mouse then peeked from the dark little hole.

10. The fawn saw a little gray mouse crawling on four paws over the straw.

Go on ➤

118

Sentence Comprehension:
Storybook 12 Assessment, page 5

Sentence Comprehension

Name _____

11. "Look!" said Paul. "There is a big leaf truck."

12. Claude and Paul have a red wagon. They tied it to their blue pedal-car.

13. Back and forth Claude and Paul went, hauling leaves.

14. Claude and Paul paused a bit and then fell onto the big pile of leaves.

15. Just then Dad clapped his hands. "You two need some applause," he said.

Go on ▶

Sentence Comprehension

16. Channing hung a bell on the top rung of a ladder.

17. Channing tapped the bell. A lovely, singing bird was set before the king!

18. The kids clapped and clapped. "We love your show!" they said.

19. Ingrid was the queen of the kingdom. She sang a long song.

20. The kids pushed Willie's big dog out from under the table.

Sentence
Comprehension

Number Correct

Sentence Comprehension:
Storybook 12 Assessment, page 7

Story Comprehension

Name _____

Claude and Paul are twins. They were seven years old in August.

Claude and Paul have a red wagon. They tied it to their blue pedal-car.

"We can help Dad haul the leaves now," said Paul.

"Yes, we can do it fast because the car will help us," said Claude.

"This is fun, but it is still hard!" said Paul.

Claude and Paul paused a bit and then fell onto the big pile of leaves.

What fun it was!

1. The twins were _____.
   - ○ ten in August
   - ○ seven in April
   - ○ six in April
   - ● seven in August

Story Comprehension

Look back if you need help.

2. Claude and Paul have a red wagon and a
   _____.

   blue bike   blue wagon   red bike   blue pedal-car
   ○   ○   ○   ●

3. The time of the year was _____.
   spring   autumn   summer   winter
   ○   ●   ○   ○

4. What was Paul and Claude's job?
   ● to haul leaves
   ○ to help Mom
   ○ to play in the leaves
   ○ to shop for a new wagon

5. What was fun for Paul and Claude?
   ● to fall in the leaves
   ○ to be twins
   ○ to be seven years old
   ○ to rake the leaves

Go on ➡

Story Comprehension:
Storybook 12 Assessment, page 9

Story Comprehension

Name _____

Carlos and Marla went to the park. Darby went, too. Carlos got six bugs in his jar. Marla got seven bugs in her jar.

"Look at the large dark green bug!" said Marla.

Down the path, Miss Sharp sat on a bench. Darby ran up to her.

Miss Sharp had red yarn in her basket. Darby barked at it. Then, with a quick nip, off he ran with the yarn!

Carlos and Marla ran to catch Darby.

At last Darby stopped. Carlos gave the yarn to Miss Sharp.

"Thank you," she said.

6. Where were Carlos and Marla?

   ○ at camp

   ● at a park

   ○ in class

   ○ at a shop

Go on

Story Comprehension

Look back if you need help.

7. They went to the park to _____.
   - ○ play ball
   - ● catch bugs
   - ○ run with Darby
   - ○ see Miss Sharp

8. Carlos got _____ bugs in his jar.

seven	ten	six	five
○	○	●	○

9. What did Darby take from Miss Sharp?

her basket	her lunch	a ball of yarn	a red ball
○	○	●	○

10. How did Miss Sharp feel when she got the yarn back?

happy	sad	mad	bad
●	○	○	○

Story
Comprehension

Number Correct

Story Comprehension:
Storybook 12 Assessment, page 11

Name _____ Date _____

Book End Assessment for
Phonetic Storybook 13

o͝o, o͞o, tion, gh

STUDENT ASSESSMENT RECORD

RACEWAY STEPS 26–27	Number Possible	Number Correct	Percentage of Mastery Score
Word Recognition Step 26A	20	_____ × 5 =	_____ %
Word Comprehension Step 26A	20	_____ × 5 =	_____ %
Word Recognition Step 26B	20	_____ × 5 =	_____ %
Word Comprehension Step 26B	20	_____ × 5 =	_____ %
Word Recognition Step 27A	20	_____ × 5 =	_____ %
Word Comprehension Step 27A	20	_____ × 5 =	_____ %
Word Recognition Step 27B	20	_____ × 5 =	_____ %
Word Comprehension Step 27B	20	_____ × 5 =	_____ %
Sentence Comprehension	25	_____ × 4 =	_____ %
Story Comprehension	10	_____ × 10 =	_____ %

Total Mastery Score

Sum of _____ % ÷ 10 _____ %

Sing, Spell, Read & Write

Word Recognition and Comprehension

1.
mood

<u>boot</u>

(booth)

2.
<u>tool</u>

(pool)

cool

3.
roof

(loop)

<u>noon</u>

4.
<u>zoo</u>

scoot

(mood)

5.
noon

(bloom)

<u>balloon</u>

6.
<u>tooth</u>

(smooth)

booth

7.
<u>spoon</u>

stoop

(scoot)

8.
shoot

<u>stool</u>

(tool)

9.
mood

<u>room</u>

(hoop)

10.
<u>choose</u>

goose

(loose)

11.
stool

(fool)

<u>pool</u>

12.
(noon)

<u>goofy</u>

spoon

13.
boot

(<u>cool</u>)

loop

14.
(balloons)

smoothed

<u>goose</u>

15.
(stoop)

hoop

<u>roof</u>

16.
<u>fool</u>

(choose)

loose

17.
school

<u>lunchroom</u>

(room)

18.
(tooth)

<u>bloom</u>

toothpaste

19.
smooth

(zoo)

<u>zookeeper</u>

20.
<u>booth</u>

balloon

(school)

Word Recognition [   ]
Number Correct

Word Comprehension [   ]
Number Correct

Word Recognition and Comprehension:
Storybook 13 Assessment, page 1

Word Recognition and Comprehension

Name _____

1. (brook) took hooks	2. (stood) wood brook	3. foot (took) wood	4. wool stood (hooks)	5. stood foot (wool)
6. wool (book) bookshelf	7. wood (foot) stood	8. (brooks) book hooks	9. wool (wood) hook	10. brooks (bookshelf) stood
11. dictionary (question) vacation	12. information (action) stations	13. (condition) information attention	14. pollution (invention) celebration	15. election (nation) question
16. (stations) vacation celebration	17. (information) invention dictionary	18. pollution constitution (attention)	19. action condition (election)	20. invention nation (vacation)

Word Recognition [   ] Number Correct

Word Comprehension [   ] Number Correct

Word Recognition and Comprehension:
Storybook 13 Assessment, page 2

Word Recognition and Comprehension

1. taught brought (ought)	**2.** knight bright (fright)	**3.** sight knight (might)	**4.** bought (thought) caught	**5.** fright tight (brought)
6. mighty taught (naughty)	**7.** (bought) brought thought	**8.** knight sight (bright)	**9.** ought bought (daughter)	**10.** (knight) frighten slight
11. thought (taught) tight	**12.** fright caught (frightened)	**13.** frightening (mighty) frighten	**14.** sight daughter (caught)	**15.** naughty (light) brought
16. daughter bright (frighten)	**17.** light naughty (tight)	**18.** (slight) frightening taught	**19.** ought (sight) might	**20.** (night) frightened caught

Word Recognition [   ]   Word Comprehension [   ]

Number Correct   Number Correct

128 **Word Recognition and Comprehension:**
Storybook 13 Assessment, page 3

Word Recognition and Comprehension

Name _____

1. (enough) laugh cough	**2.** sleigh (straight) eighty	**3.** neighbor rough (neigh)	**4.** (eighty) cough though	**5.** straight (neighbor) tough
6. (sleigh) weigh neighed	**7.** eighteen (neighborhood) eighty	**8.** laugh (tough) weight	**9.** (rough) neigh neighbor	**10.** (neighed) eighty straight
11. (eight) enough through	**12.** (neighbors) neighborhood eighteen	**13.** through (though) enough	**14.** neighbors (coughed) neighed	**15.** (weigh) rough eighty
16. (eighteen) straight neighbors	**17.** though coughed (through)	**18.** (weight) eight sleigh	**19.** neighbors tough (laugh)	**20.** (cough) rough coughed

Word Recognition [ ] Number Correct

Word Comprehension [ ] Number Correct

Word Recognition and Comprehension:
Storybook 13 Assessment, page 4

129

Sentence Comprehension

1. "Here is Mother Goose. Maybe she will tell us a story," said Janet.

2. "There are polar bears. They like the cool water."

3. "Here we are at the zoo. We can buy our tickets at this booth," said Dad.

4. "There is the zookeeper with some food for the monkey."

5. "Watch the seals swim in that pool. The seal on the stool has a balloon."

Go on ➡

Sentence Comprehension:
Storybook 13 Assessment, page 5

Name _____

6. Mom had fixed Tom's food.
Tom sat in the booth to eat it.

7. "Come see, Mom!" said Tom.
"My loose tooth came out!"

8. Tom showed Beth his tooth.

9. At noon the children had lunch.
They ate in the lunchroom
at school.

10. Tom sat on a stool to play
Pop the Balloons.

Go on ➡

Sentence Comprehension

11. Ms. Brooks said, "It is time to choose. You may choose whatever you want to do in class."

12. Darrel took a book. Patty, Jody, and Donna took books, too.

13. Steve and Annie picked a game. The game is Hook-a-Fish.

14. Alonzo stood on the "V" block. Jenny stood on the "B" block. Sally stood on the "S" block.

15. "May we paint?" asked Paul.

Go on

Sentence Comprehension

Name _____

16. The United States is our nation.

17. The Constitution was made by the leaders who started our nation.

18. Our leaders speak on TV stations. They give us information.

19. We go to places where we can vote for the leaders we want to have.

20. On the Fourth of July we have a celebration. It is during summer vacation.

Go on ▶

21. Once there was a huge dragon. He thought it was fun to frighten people.

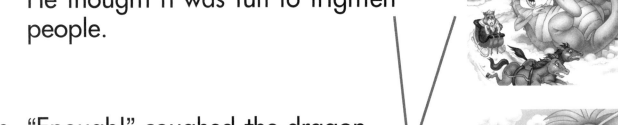

22. "Enough!" coughed the dragon. "It was a good tennis match," said the knight.

23. Princess Sara's horses neighed in fright and ran home.

24. "I will stop frightening people if you beat me at a game," said the dragon.

25. King Tweek sent a tough knight to stop the dragon. "You are mean to frighten people," said the knight.

Sentence
Comprehension

Number Correct

Sentence Comprehension:
Storybook 13 Assessment, page 9

Story Comprehension

Name _____

The United States is our nation.

In the United States we choose our leaders. We choose them on Election Day. We go to places where we can vote.

Our leaders speak on TV stations. They give us information. They tell us about the condition of our nation. They tell us what they will do. They ask us to vote for them.

1. The United States is our _____.

leader	nation	law	station
○	●	○	○

2. When do we choose our leaders?
   - ○ on our birthday
   - ○ on New Year's Day
   - ● on Election Day
   - ○ on July 4th

3. People will vote on Election Day.

   Yes   No
   ●   ○

Go on →

Look back if you need help.

4. We elect people and they become our
_____.

girls   twins   leaders   nations

○   ○   ●   ○

5. Election Day is _____.

○ not an important day

● an important day

○ a silly day

○ a day to play

Go on

© Pearson Education, Inc./Modern Curriculum Press/Pearson Learning Group. All rights reserved. Copying strictly prohibited.

Story Comprehension

Name _____

The laws of the United States are in a list. The list of laws is called the Constitution.

The Constitution was a new invention. It was made by the leaders who started our nation. The laws of the Constitution give us freedom.

6. What is the list of laws called?
   - ○ The List of Laws
   - ○ The U.S. Laws
   - ○ The invention
   - ● The Constitution

7. Who made the Constitution?
   - ● the leaders who started our nation
   - ○ our teacher
   - ○ the boys and girls
   - ○ our leaders we have now

Go on ➡️

Story Comprehension

Look back if you need help.

8. What did the Constitution give us?

candy   leaders   freedom   inventions

○   ○   ●   ○

9. The Constitution is the law of our _____.

school   nation   class   town

○   ●   ○   ○

10. This story is about _____.
    - ○ the leaders
    - ○ a teacher
    - ● the Constitution
    - ○ boys and girls

Story Comprehension
[ ]
Number Correct

Assessment — Raceway Steps 28A-C

Name _____   Date _____

Book End Assessment for
Phonetic Storybook 14

all, ar = or, dge, ue, le, x = cks,
ie = ē, ęā, ĕą, eąr = er, f to v + es

STUDENT ASSESSMENT RECORD				
RACEWAY STEPS 28A–C	**Number Possible**	**Number Correct**	**Percentage of Mastery Score**	
Word Recognition Step 28A	20	_____ × 5 =	_____ %	
Word Comprehension Step 28A	20	_____ × 5 =	_____ %	
Word Recognition Step 28B	20	_____ × 5 =	_____ %	
Word Comprehension Step 28B	20	_____ × 5 =	_____ %	
Word Recognition Step 28C	20	_____ × 5 =	_____ %	
Word Comprehension Step 28C	20	_____ × 5 =	_____ %	
Sentence Comprehension	25	_____ × 4 =	_____ %	**Total Mastery Score**
Story Comprehension	10	_____ × 10 =	_____ %	
			Sum of _____ % ÷ 8	_____ %

Word Recognition and Comprehension

1.
wall
(hall)
call

2.
(reward)
swarmed
toward

3.
bridge
sledge
(wedged)

4.
true
(flue)
due

5.
thwart
pledge
(small)

6.
(warm)
war
wall

7.
hall
(giggle)
edge

8.
pledge
(ledge)
budge

9.
(call)
clue
glue

10.
nudged
(budge)
Sue

11.
fall
(warned)
wedged

12.
(due)
clue
war

13.
trudged
little
(middle)

14.
Hodges
(bridge)
hedge

15.
(trudged)
flue
fall

16.
Warren
warned
(true)

17.
hue
(edge)
ridge

18.
(wall)
small
basketball

19.
warm
sledge
(hedge)

20.
edge
pledge
(glue)

Word Recognition ☐ Number Correct

Word Comprehension ☐ Number Correct

Word Recognition and Comprehension:
Storybook 14 Assessment, page 1

Word Recognition and Comprehension

Name _____

1. (ax) / <u>ox</u> / mixed	**2.** (niece) / <u>believed</u> / pier
3. <u>bear</u> / pear / (great)	**4.** <u>relax</u> / (field) / shield
5. piece / (relief) / disbelief	

6. <u>pear</u> / steak / (break)	**7.** <u>great</u> / (mixed) / relax
8. <u>pier</u> / brief / (shield)	**9.** <u>mixed</u> / relief / (ox)
10. <u>brief</u> / (piece) / pier	

11. (chief) / yield / <u>niece</u>	**12.** great / (believed) / <u>disbelief</u>
13. (relax) / <u>relief</u> / great	**14.** piece / (pear) / <u>shield</u>
15. (brief) / bear / <u>break</u>	

16. (wear) / <u>ax</u> / chief	**17.** ox / <u>mixing</u> / (pier)
18. (steak) / <u>field</u> / shield	**19.** disbelief / (niece) / <u>Greenfield</u>
20. yield / (bear) / <u>steak</u>	

Word Recognition [ ] Number Correct

Word Comprehension [ ] Number Correct

Word Recognition and Comprehension:
Storybook 14 Assessment, page 2

141

Word Recognition and Comprehension

1. sweater <u>weather</u> (feather)	**2.** <u>early</u> learned (earned)	**3.** loaf wives (Earl)	**4.** read <u>heard</u> (head)	**5.** <u>thieves'</u> (lives) wives
6. Heather <u>health</u> (breath)	**7.** (loaves) <u>knife</u> search	**8.** <u>head</u> (thread) searched	**9.** <u>pearls</u> heard (search)	**10.** ready (steady) <u>heavy</u>
11. <u>sweater</u> (wife) dead	**12.** <u>thread</u> (thieves') searched	**13.** <u>learned</u> (loaf) loaves	**14.** (heavy) <u>heard</u> health	**15.** lives <u>wives</u> (weather)
16. (pearls) dead <u>feather</u>	**17.** <u>read</u> (ready) steady	**18.** sweater <u>Heather</u> (sweaters)	**19.** <u>breath</u> (learned) knife	**20.** Earl (early) <u>earned</u>

Word Recognition		Word Comprehension	
	Number Correct		Number Correct

Word Recognition and Comprehension:
Storybook 14 Assessment, page 3

Sentence Comprehension

Name _____

1. "May we go out in the boat today?"
   Heather asked.
   "Yes," said Mom. "Put on your sweaters.
   It is still cool."

2. Skip picked up the net and stretched
   to get the crab. "Oh, it is dead,"
   he said.

3. "Oops!" said Skip. "A thread in my
   sweater is caught on a splinter."

4. Just then a seagull flew over the boat.
   A feather floated down onto Heather's
   head.

5. "Look!" cried Skip. "They are getting
   a fish!"

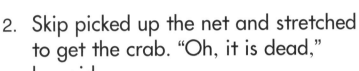

Go on ➤

Sentence Comprehension

6. Sue wrote, "It is true, I love you." on each one.

7. "This silver paper sometimes looks blue and sometimes yellow!" said Sue.

8. Sue had to hurry to the mailbox with her valentines.

9. Sue's mom opened the fireplace flue.

10. Sue did not put her name on the valentines, but she gave this clue: 19-21-5.

Go on →

Sentence Comprehension:
Storybook 14 Assessment, page 5

Sentence Comprehension

Name _____

11. Ramon swept the steps. David pulled weeds from the lawn.

12. Mrs. Hodges gave the boys a big hug.

13. Ramon and David were glad they had fixed up her yard.

14. Ramon lifted some tools out of the way.

15. David and Ramon finished. Then, they trudged back to the shed with their tools. _____

Go on →

Sentence Comprehension

16. Warren was a traveler who had no fear. He came from a planet not far from here.

17. "Let's be friends," he said with a smile.

18. Warren landed on a strange, warm world.

19. Safe on a beach, Warren lay down. Soon little animals swarmed all around.

20. A brave animal came toward Warren and said, "Tie up this creature with a long, strong cord."

Go on ➡

Sentence Comprehension

Name _____

21. Grandmother had a shap knife. She cut some slices from one loaf for them.

22. "When we finish raking these leaves, I will tell you the story," said Grandfather.

23. "They gave both chests to a museum because there were so many gems."

24. Grandmother called from the porch.

25. "Sam and Ben and their wives dove back down to search for more pearls."

Sentence
Comprehension [   ]

Number Correct

Sentence Comprehension:
Storybook 14 Assessment, page 8

Story Comprehension

   The basketball coach was going to pick the team today. All the kids wanted to be on the team to play in the fall. They waited in the hall to see the coach. Some sat on benches, and some leaned on the wall. The tall kids were sure they would be picked.

   The not-so-tall kids hoped to be on the team, too. Nick was not-so-tall. He was small, but he played basketball very well. He wished Coach Dobbs would pick him to be on the team.

1. Will all the kids be picked to be on the team?

   Yes   No

   ○   ●

2. Where did the kids wait?

   ○   in a classroom

   ●   in the hall

   ○   at Coach Dobbs's house

   ○   at home

3. Which word does <u>not</u> belong?

   basketball   Coach Dobbs   team   paint

   ○   ○   ○   ●

Go on

Story Comprehension:
Storybook 14 Assessment, page 9

Story Comprehension

Name _____

Look back if you need help.

4. Who would pick the team?
   - ○ the teacher
   - ○ the boys and girls
   - ○ the moms and dads
   - ● Coach Dobbs

5. Who played basketball very well?
   - ○ only the tall kids
   - ● Nick
   - ○ Coach Dobbs
   - ○ the not-so-tall kids

Go on ▶

Story Comprehension

Uncle Max said, "Could you stir this paint and mix it well for me? It is thick and lumpy."

"Sure," said Tony. He was glad to help. Tony started mixing the paint.

After awhile, Uncle Max looked to see if the paint was mixed.

"Well," said Uncle Max, "I would say you are as strong as an ox and as smart as a fox! With such good help, we can be finished before six o'clock!"

6. Who were working together?

   ○ Tony and Jack

   ○ Uncle Max and Jack

   ● Tony and Uncle Max

   ○ Jack and Sam

7. Will Tony and Uncle Max be finished today?

   Yes   No

   ●   ○

8. How did Uncle Max feel?

   ○ sad because the paint spilled

   ● happy because Tony did a good job

   ○ mad because he could not paint

   ○ silly because Tony was stronger

Story Comprehension

Name _____

Look back if you need help.

9. Because Tony helped Uncle Max, the job was finished
   _____.

   quickly   slowly   late   yesterday
   ●   ○   ○   ○

10. Uncle Max said Tony was as strong as _____
    and as smart as _____.

    ○ a dog, a cat

    ● an ox, a fox

    ○ a fox, an ox

    ○ a man, a teacher

Story
Comprehension [   ]

Number Correct

Name _____ Date _____

Book End Assessment for
Phonetic Storybook 15

Long ī, long ō, u = ŏŏ, air, ui = ōō, or = er, contractions, āre = air, ä = ŏ, c = s

STUDENT ASSESSMENT RECORD

RACEWAY STEPS 29–30	Number Possible	Number Correct	Percentage of Mastery Score	
Word Recognition Step 29	20	_____ × 5 =	_____ %	
Word Comprehension Step 29	20	_____ × 5 =	_____ %	
Word Recognition Step 30A	20	_____ × 5 =	_____ %	
Word Comprehension Step 30A	20	_____ × 5 =	_____ %	
Word Recognition Step 30B	20	_____ × 5 =	_____ %	
Word Comprehension Step 30B	20	_____ × 5 =	_____ %	
Sentence Comprehension	20	_____ × 5 =	_____ %	Total
Story Comprehension	10	_____ × 10 =	_____ %	Mastery Score
			Sum of _____ % ÷ 8 _____ %	

Sing, Spell Read&Write

Word Recognition and Comprehension

1.
(behind)
kind
mind

2.
air
hair
(fair)

3.
(chair)
cushion
juice

4.
(nuisance)
suit
pair

5.
fair
bull
(cushion)

6.
full
(bushy)
bull

7.
suit
(fruit)
hold

8.
(kind)
fair
full

9.
chair
air
(pair)

10.
(mind)
fruit
cushion

11.
chair
nuisance
(suit)

12.
old
(air)
juice

13.
behind
bull
(full)

14.
(hair)
mind
bushy

15.
kind
fruit
(stair)

16.
mind
(cold)
pair

17.
kind
juice
(bull)

18.
full
hair
(old)

19.
stair
fair
(juice)

20.
(hold)
behind
cold

Word Recognition

Number Correct

Word Comprehension

Number Correct

154 **Word Recognition and Comprehension:**
Storybook 15 Assessment, page 1

Word Recognition and Comprehension

Name _____

1. (tailor) tutor sailor	2. (didn't) there's you're	3. operator (elevator) you'd	4. (inventor) doctor janitor	5. (conductor) sculptor professor
6. (doctor) mayor actor	7. (aren't) we're we'll	8. actor inventor (tutor)	9. (sailor) elevator they're	10. author janitor (mayor)
11. you'd didn't (we're)	12. (professor) we're doctor	13. (motor) conductor mayor	14. (there's) they're you're	15. sculptor (author) visitor
16. tutor (janitor) aren't	17. tailor (sculptor) sailor	18. professor inventor (operator)	19. elevator conductor (visitor)	20. we'll (they're) you're

Word Recognition [   ]
Number Correct

Word Comprehension [   ]
Number Correct

Word Recognition and Comprehension:
Storybook 15 Assessment, page 2

Word Recognition and Comprehension

1. bare (dare) fare	2. fancy (cider) center	3. Aha washed (Ha, ha)	4. share (scared) stared	5. rare blare (flare)
6. (peace) voices rejoice	7. (swamp) dancing watt	8. spare (share) care	9. prince (concerts) fancy	10. (watt) wasp washed
11. scared (city) swamp	12. (stared) father peace	13. cider celebration (voices)	14. flare (rare) fare	15. (center) concerts bare
16. rejoice Aha (care)	17. prance (wasp) dare	18. (spare) swamp scared	19. (washed) watt wasp	20. (dancing) celebration share

Word Recognition [ ] Number Correct

Word Comprehension [ ] Number Correct

156 **Word Recognition and Comprehension:**
Storybook 15 Assessment, page 3

Sentence Comprehension

Name _____

1. Do you want to be a janitor or an elevator operator?

2. Would you like to be a music conductor? Would you like to be a tutor helping a student?

3. If you are an author, you may see your name on banners.

4. Do you want to be an actor, or do you want to be an inventor?

5. If you choose to be a doctor, you can take care of people when they get sick!

Go on

6. It was a fair day. Tim went outside to read a book.

7. A squirrel with a bushy tail was on the chair. The chair was a mess. It was full of nut shells.

8. When Tim came out, he spilled the juice! It splashed on Dad's suit!

9. The wind was blowing hard now. The air blew Tim's hair. It blew the pages.

10. After Tim cleaned the chair, he sat down to read.

Go on ➡

Sentence Comprehension

Name _____

11. Once there was a little wasp named Buzzy. He lived in a big swamp.

12. "It is just an old 100-watt light bulb!"

13. Father and Buzzy washed the thing. They washed it with swamp water.

14. "Father," said Buzzy. "I've found something that is like the moon!"

15. Then, Father Wasp began to laugh, "Ha, ha!"

Go on →

Sentence Comprehension:
Storybook 15 Assessment, page 6

Sentence Comprehension

16. "Would anyone like to visit the natural history museum?" asked Mom.

17. "There is a crowd ahead. We will wind our way around them," said Mom.

18. "We will need our jackets. It is cold outside," said Mom.

19. "Wow! Look at that dinosaur! What kind is it?" asked Iris.

20. "Let's stay together and keep to the side of the sidewalk," said Mom.

Sentence Comprehension

Number Correct

Story Comprehension

Name _____

What do you want to be when you grow up?

Do you want to be an actor, or do you want to be an inventor?

Do you want to be a janitor or an elevator operator?

Think about it. Choose something you enjoy doing. Then, do your job well!

Would you like to be a music conductor?

Would you like to be a tutor helping a student?

You could be a mayor. You could be a sailor and work on a ship.

1. This story is about _____.

    ○ going to school

    ● jobs when you grow up

    ○ a day at the zoo

    ○ time to play

2. Which word does not belong?

conductor	enjoy	tutor	janitor
○	●	○	○

Go on ➡

Story Comprehension

Look back if you need help.

3. Pick the job listed <u>in this story</u>.

inspector   king   painter   inventor

○   ○   ○   ●

4. If you want to help a student, you can be a
   _____.

conductor   tutor   janitor   mayor

○   ●   ○   ○

5. If you enjoy your job, you will feel _____.

happy   sad   silly   mad

●   ○   ○   ○

Go on ➡

Story Comprehension

Name _____

We had just paid the fare at the toll booth and were back on the highway.

"Oh no! A flat tire!" said Dad.

"Take care," said Mom. "We don't dare stop here. We must get to the side of the road."

Dad lit a flare so other drivers could see us. He took the spare tire from the trunk. Dad said I could help. It made me feel good to share the work.

6. When did they get a flat?
   - ○ before paying the toll fare
   - ● just after paying the toll fare
   - ○ on the highway
   - ○ on the driveway at home

7. Where did they stop to fix the tire?
   - ○ at the toll booth
   - ○ on the road
   - ○ at the gas station
   - ● at the side of the road

Go on

Story Comprehension:
Storybook 15 Assessment, page 10   **163**

Story Comprehension

Look back if you need help.

8. Why did Dad light the flare?

   ● so the other drivers could see them

   ○ so Dad could see in the dark

   ○ because Robby liked flares

   ○ they needed some heat

9. Where did Dad find the spare tire?

   ○ at the gas station

   ○ in the woods

   ○ on the back seat

   ● in the trunk

10. Do you think they finished their trip?

    Yes   No

    ●   ○

Story Comprehension

Number Correct

Story Comprehension:
Storybook 15 Assessment, page 9

Name _____ Date _____

Book End Assessment for
Phonetic Storybook 16

silent w, k, l, b, g, h, t, qu = k

STUDENT ASSESSMENT RECORD			
RACEWAY STEPS 31–33	**Number Possible**	**Number Correct**	**Percentage of Mastery Score**
Word Recognition Step 31	20	_____ × 5 =	_____ %
Word Comprehension Step 31	20	_____ × 5 =	_____ %
Word Recognition Step 32	20	_____ × 5 =	_____ %
Word Comprehension Step 32	20	_____ × 5 =	_____ %
Word Recognition Step 33	20	_____ × 5 =	_____ %
Word Comprehension Step 33	20	_____ × 5 =	_____ %
Sentence Comprehension	20	_____ × 5 =	_____ %
Story Comprehension	10	_____ × 10 =	_____ %

Total Mastery Score

Sum of _____ % ÷ 8 _____ %

Word Recognition and Comprehension

1. write (wrote) wrap	2. knot knelt (knocked)	3. writing (wreath) wrinkles	4. knapsack (knowledge) knuckles	5. (wrong) wrench written
6. knitted (known) knew	7. wrote (written) wrong	8. (knob) knees knew	9. (Wright) wrote doorknob	10. wrap (knelt) knit
11. (wrench) writing known	12. (wrinkles) written knowledge	13. wristwatch knit (wrap)	14. wrench knapsack (Knotsville)	15. (knot) wrong wreath
16. knuckles wrap (writing)	17. doorknob (knitted) known	18. (knit) Wright knob	19. (knees) wristwatch knocked	20. (knuckles) wreath wrench

Word Recognition [ ] Number Correct

Word Comprehension [ ] Number Correct

Word Recognition and Comprehension:
Storybook 16 Assessment, page 1

Word Recognition and Comprehension

Name _____

1. (salve) talk <u>walk</u>	**2.** (crumb) numb <u>comb</u>	**3.** debt <u>salmon</u> (talk)	**4.** (limb) comb <u>lamb</u>	**5.** salve <u>folks</u> (calf)
6. <u>calm</u> (half) palm	**7.** <u>plumber</u> doubted (walked)	**8.** (should) half <u>palm</u>	**9.** crumb (debt) <u>limb</u>	**10.** (stalk) <u>talking</u> comb
11. <u>thumb</u> folks (palm)	**12.** calm <u>crumb</u> (salmon)	**13.** limb <u>half</u> (calm)	**14.** (walk) <u>should</u> numb	**15.** calf <u>doubted</u> (lamb)
16. (folks) <u>talk</u> stalk	**17.** <u>numb</u> (doubted) limb	**18.** <u>salve</u> salmon (plumber)	**19.** talk <u>debt</u> (talking)	**20.** should (comb) <u>walked</u>

Word Recognition ☐ Number Correct

Word Comprehension ☐ Number Correct

Word Recognition and Comprehension

1. (gnu) gnarl gnaw	2. hustle listen (bustle)	3. mosquitoes (antique) bouquet	4. glisten (bristles) gristle	5. John (gnats) gnus
6. gnawing (moisten) honor	7. hustle (rustle) gristle	8. croquet (bouquet) bustle	9. moisten thistle (whistle)	10. often (listen) antique
11. gnarl (glisten) bristles	12. (John) rustle croquet	13. glisten whistle (thistledown)	14. gnats (mosquitoes) often	15. (honor) sign listen
16. hustle thistle (often)	17. gnaw (Thomas) gnus	18. bristles gristle (Rhonda)	19. (gnawing) bouquet assigned	20. thistledown moisten (thistle)

Word Recognition [ ] Number Correct

Word Comprehension [ ] Number Correct

Word Recognition and Comprehension:
Storybook 16 Assessment, page 3

168

Sentence Comprehension

Name _____

1. One hot day, three large gnus gnawed on plants and grass. They swished their tails to keep the gnats away.

2. Next to the sign, there was an old tree. There, in the gnarl of the tree, sat a monkey.

3. Suddenly, the three gnus heard a soft voice call.

4. "Hop on my back," said Gomer Gnu. With a swish of his tail, Gomer ran by the sign with the little monkey on his strong back.

5. The call came from near the sign that said Gnu Crossing.

Go on ➤

6. Gary Goldfinch sat on his limb. The air was getting cold. Gary was getting cold.

7. Suddenly, a big gust of wind smacked Gary! It hit him hard, and he fell to the ground.

8. Gary packed his bag. He put in his comb and his last few crumbs.

9. "Climb in," said Ray. "You can ride here with me."

10. "Would you give me a ride south, where it doesn't snow?" Gary asked the lamb.

Go on

Sentence Comprehension

Name _____

11. Dad and Pam went fishing.
"Talking could scare the fish," said Dad.
"Sh," said Pam to the moose calf.

12. Pam walked by a plant with three leaves on its stems. Soon, Pam felt an itch. The itch was on the calf of Pam's leg.

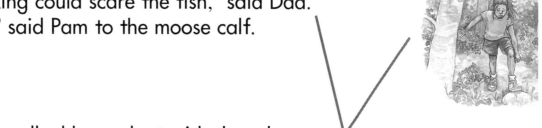

13. Pam and her folks went for a walk.

14. Pam went with her folks. They drove in the car for half the day. They drove to the country.

15. They camped near a big lake. "This is a calm and peaceful place," said Dad.

Go on ➤

Sentence Comprehension:
Storybook 16 Assessment, page 6

Sentence Comprehension

16. Queen Bee is blowing her shiny new whistle!
    She's calling the bees from the clover and
    thistle!

17. "Listen! Mosquitoes! Listen! Stand guard!
    Don't let strange bugs come into our yard!"

18. Who's that riding the big dragonfly?
    Wave hello to King John as he goes by!

19. "Thomas, be sure no gristle is left on the
    meat! Rhonda, please set up a game
    of croquet."

20. "Get brushes with bristles and scrub all
    the floors.
    Moisten some sponges and wipe walls
    and doors."

Sentence
Comprehension

Number Correct

Sentence Comprehension:
Storybook 16 Assessment, page 7

172

Story Comprehension

Name _____

There is an old barn in a small town called Knotsville. Lots of animals live in the barn. Some of the animals only come out at night.

Nan is well known to the animals in the barn. She comes every day to feed and milk each cow. She brings her lunch in a knapsack. When she is finished with lunch, she hangs the knapsack on the doorknob.

One day the knapsack had a loose button. Nan did not know the button was loose. As Nan took the knapsack off the knob, the button fell off. Mel and Max Mouse saw it fall.

Nan took a step. She knocked the button across the floor. It fell into a crack.

Nan knelt down. She tried to reach the button. The crack was too tight. Her knuckles did not fit.

1. What is Knotsville?

   an old barn　　　　a cow　　　　a small town　　　　a lake
     ○　　　　　　　　　○　　　　　　　　●　　　　　　　　○

2. Does Nan go to the barn every day?

   Yes　　　　　　No
    ●　　　　　　　○

Go on

Look back if you need help.

3. What does Nan bring her lunch in?

a bag ○   a pail ○   a knapsack ●   a box ○

4. Which word does not belong?

Nan ○   cow ○   barn ○   store ●

5. What does Nan do in the barn?

○ sweeps the floor

● feeds and milks each cow

○ fixes a doorknob

○ visits Mel and Max

6. Did Nan know the button was loose?

Yes ○   No ●

7. Who saw the button fall?

an owl ○   a spider ○   a cow ○   two mice ●

Story Comprehension:
Storybook 16 Assessment, page 9

Story Comprehension

Name _____

Look back if you need help.

8. Where did the button go?
   - ○ It fell into the milk.
   - ● It fell into a crack.
   - ○ It rolled out the door.
   - ○ It rolled into the knapsack.

9. What did Nan do?
   - ○ She went home.
   - ○ She ate her lunch.
   - ● She tried to reach the button.
   - ○ She took a nap.

10. Do you think the animals in the barn like Nan?

    Yes   No

    ●   ○

Story
Comprehension [_____]

Number Correct

Name _____   Date _____

Book End Assessment for
Phonetic Storybook 17

ph = f, ch = k, ss = sh, borrowers and wacky words,
t = ch, ch = sh, ous, multisyllable words

STUDENT ASSESSMENT RECORD

RACEWAY STEPS 34–36	Number Possible	Number Correct	Percentage of Mastery Score	
Word Recognition Step 34	20	_____ × 5 =	_____ %	
Word Comprehension Step 34	20	_____ × 5 =	_____ %	
Word Recognition Step 35	20	_____ × 5 =	_____ %	
Word Comprehension Step 35	20	_____ × 5 =	_____ %	
Word Recognition Step 36	20	_____ × 5 =	_____ %	
Word Comprehension Step 36	20	_____ × 5 =	_____ %	
Sentence Comprehension	25	_____ × 4 =	_____ %	Total Mastery Score
Story Comprehension	10	_____ × 10 =	_____ %	
		Sum of _____ % ÷ 8	_____ %	

Sing, Spell Read & Write.

Word Recognition and Comprehension

1. dolphins (phooey) photos	2. chef (chaise) parachute	3. (mission) permission discussion	4. christen (chrome) chorus	5. (Stephanie) Joseph dolphins
6. Charlotte chandelier (Chicago)	7. schedule (chords) anchor	8. trophy Phoenix (photos)	9. Chris admission (ache)	10. photographs (autographs) Philadelphia
11. stomach (session) christen	12. (Phoenix) mission gophers	13. (chrome) schedule Chris	14. (telephone) Michelle alphabet	15. Chalfonte chauffeur (chandelier)
16. (anchor) Michigan stomach	17. (schedule) parachute crochet	18. alphabet (gophers) telephone	19. discussion (permission) admission	20. (chorus) Cheryl chords

Word Recognition [ ] Number Correct

Word Comprehension [ ] Number Correct

178 **Word Recognition and Comprehension:**
Storybook 17 Assessment, page 1

Word Recognition and Comprehension

Name _____

1. (soup) sugar does	2. heart (build) done	3. sergeants creatures (guided)	4. maple friend (brother)	5. (medicine) village build
6. poured ocean (friend)	7. creatures vegetable (Wednesday)	8. (colonel) leather build	9. (does) guided soup	10. syrup sugar (sergeants)
11. lieutenant (heart) maple	12. (syrup) soup colonel	13. (poured) pizza medicine	14. sergeants Wednesday (nature)	15. vegetable maple (village)
16. (guided) medicine syrup	17. does lieutenant (leather)	18. (pizza) poured village	19. brother (vegetable) learning	20. (ocean) eyes nature

Word Recognition ☐ Number Correct

Word Comprehension ☐ Number Correct

Word Recognition and Comprehension:
Storybook 17 Assessment, page 2

179

Word Recognition and Comprehension

1. enormous (explanation) subtraction	**2.** (famous) fabulous tomorrow	**3.** cafeteria detective (commotion)	**4.** curious (generous) congratulations	**5.** equipment famous (tomorrow)
6. (dangerous) yesterday department	**7.** (investigation) curious cafeteria	**8.** gorgeous generous (fabulous)	**9.** investigation (together) equipment	**10.** apartment (location) detective
11. homework curious (gorgeous)	**12.** yesterday commotion (congratulations)	**13.** (enormous) investigation subtraction	**14.** (yesterday) famous dangerous	**15.** location gorgeous (cafeteria)
16. dangerous (detective) explanation	**17.** elevator apartment (department)	**18.** (equipment) generous location	**19.** cafeteria commotion (subtraction)	**20.** enormous tomorrow (apartment)

Word
Recognition

Number Correct

Word
Comprehension

Number Correct

180

Word Recognition and Comprehension:
Storybook 17 Assessment, page 3

Sentence Comprehension

Name _____

1. True Heart can make his own shoes. They are made of leather.

2. When True Heart walks in the forest, he is sure of all the paths.

3. True Heart likes all the creatures in the woods.

4. It was a maple tree. Sap was dripping from a broken branch.

5. On a Wednesday in early spring, two deer came to True Heart. One of the deer did not look well.

Go on ➤

Sentence Comprehension

6. Joseph and Stephanie did their homework and wrote the alphabet.

7. It was a rainy day.
"Phooey!" said Joseph.
"Phooey!" said Stephanie.

8. There would be no autographs on the photos.

9. Then, the telephone rang.
"Telephone!" called Mom. "It's Dad."

10. "The rain will stop. I'll close the shop," said Dad.

Go on ➤

Sentence Comprehension:
Storybook 17 Assessment, page 5

Name _____

11. There was even a movie theater with no admission charge!

12. "I feel funny," said Chris. "I have a stomachache."

13. Chris had permission to hold the ship's wheel and wear the captain's hat.

14. Up came the huge anchor.

15. Chris sang in a chorus with the other children on the ship.

Go on ➡

Sentence Comprehension

16. Four friends can have fun. They like to play Secret Spy.

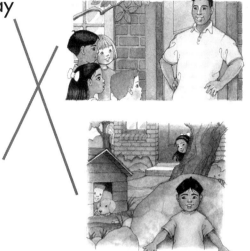

17. Tim's dad was at the door. "Did you have fun?" he asked.

18. Judd and Carly helped build a campsite.

19. Then, they saw some tracks!

20. Suddenly, they heard many noises! Their hearts began to thump!

Go on ➡

Sentence Comprehension

Name _____

21. Bobby was curious. What was going on in the school cafeteria?

22. "What an enormous cake! It's gorgeous!" cried Bobby.

23. Bobby told Rick about the Keep Out! sign on the door of the school cafeteria.

24. The next day Rick and Bobby's class had a great celebration.

25. "Before we go, we need to gather my detective equipment," said Rick.

Sentence
Comprehension [   ]

Number Correct

Sentence Comprehension:
Storybook 17 Assessment, page 8

Story Comprehension

Four friends can have fun. They can play together. Judd, Carly, Nissa, and Tim are friends. They like to play Secret Spy.

Tim is the biggest. He is going to be the colonel. Carly will be the lieutenant. Judd and Nissa are to be sergeants.

Judd and Carly helped build a campsite. Tim and Nissa poured soup from the thermos. It is easy if everyone works together.

Judd, Carly, Tim, and Nissa went on a hike in the yard. They climbed on some rocks. Then, they saw some tracks! After that the friends played Secret Spy. Suddenly, they heard many noises! Their hearts began to thump!

"Oh, Rex! You sure did fool us! We are so glad it's you!" said the children.

Soon, it was time to go inside. Tim's dad was at the door.

"Did you have fun?" he asked. "Mom has some vegetable pizza for you and your friends. It is hot from the oven!"

1. Mom has just taken the pizza from the oven, so it is
   _____.

warm	cold	hot	cool
○	○	●	○

2. What did the friends like to play?

Secret Spy	Tug-of-War	baseball	janitor
●	○	○	○

Go on

186 **Story Comprehension:**
Storybook 17 Assessment, page 9

Story Comprehension

Name _____

Look back if you need help.

3. Building a campsite and pouring soup was easy because
   _____.

   ○ the children liked each other

   ● the children worked together

   ○ it was raining

   ○ the children did not like each other

4. When did they see the tracks?

   ○ before lunch

   ○ at night

   ● after they climbed on some rocks

   ○ after they heard some noises

5. What made the noise that frightened the children?

   ○ an owl

   ○ a gopher

   ○ a bear

   ● Rex, the dog

Go on →

Story Comprehension

Look back if you need help.

6. Why did they go inside?

   ○ There was no place else to go.

   ○ It was raining.

   ● It was time to go.

   ○ It was getting dark.

7. Who was the colonel?

Carly	Judd	Nissa	Tim
○	○	○	●

8. What did Tim and Nissa pour soup from?

   ○ a glass

   ○ a pot

   ● a thermos

   ○ a mug

9. Could this story be true?

Yes	No
●	○

Go on

Story Comprehension

Name _____

Look back if you need help.

10. A good name for this story is _____.

   ○ "Mom, Dad, and the Pizza"

   ● "Four Friends Have Fun"

   ○ "Rex the Dog"

   ○ "Soup for Supper"

You can read anything you want. Isn't that great?
Congratulations!

Story Comprehension ⬚

Number Correct

Student Record Sheet for

Sing, Spell, Read&Write®

Achievement Test #1
(To be administered orally)

STUDENT ASSESSMENT RECORD

Student's Name _____   Grade _____   Date _____

Teacher's Name _____   School _____

Examiner's Name _____   Mastery Score _____/%

Total for Section A: _____ /24

Total for Section B: _____ /20

Total for Section C: _____ /20

Total for Section D: _____ /36

TOTAL: _____% of Mastery Score

Achievement Test #1

SECTION A: Letter Names & Sounds — Raceway Steps 1-3

Have student give the name and sound of each letter. Allow 5 seconds per item. Draw a line through each miscue.

Mm	D	s	o
Hh	R	p	e
Nn	T	w	a
Jj	L	b	u
Ff	V	k	i
Ll	Z	y	a
_____/6	_____/6	_____/6	_____/6

Total for SECTION A: _____/24

SECTION B: Blends & Words — Raceway Steps 4-14

Have student give the sound of the letter blend. Allow 5 seconds per item. Draw a line through each miscue.

ba	pi	ten	block
be	mo	jog	dress
bi	fa	ran	truck
bo	ne	dug	flip
bu	mu	bit	stand
_____/5	_____/5	_____/5	_____/5

Total for SECTION B: _____/20

SECTION C: Vocabulary Words — Raceway Steps 6-15

Have student read each word. Allow 5 seconds per word. Draw a line through each miscue.

went	camp	as	was
must	grand	the	to
bend	cannot	is	said
stick	flop	a	of
milk	swam	his	have
_____/5	_____/5	_____/5	_____/5

Total for SECTION B: _____/20

SECTION D: Sentences — Raceway Steps 6-15

Have student read each sentence. Allow 5 seconds per word. Draw a line through each miscue. Subtract the number of miscues from 36 points.

1. A man had ham and jam.
2. Nan can mend the bent pen.
3. Dad will help Jim a bit.
4. Spot got the doll from the pot.
5. Gus had a lot of fun in the mud.
6. West Camp has a pond.

Total for SECTION D: _____/36

Achievement Test #2

This test can be used at the end of first grade to assess how well a student has mastered the 36 Steps of the Level 1 program. After administering and scoring the test, use the chart on page 196 to see where the student might need extra help.

This test can also be used to place a child in the grade 1 program. After administering and scoring the test, use the chart on page 196 to see at what step instruction should begin for that student.

Directions

1. Tear out both the Student Record Sheet on page 194 and Achievement Test #2 on page 195.

2. Fill out the student information at the top of the Student Record Sheet.

3. Have the student sit at a table opposite the examiner and place Achievement Test #2 in front of the student.

4. Ask the student to read the words in List #1 aloud. Point out that the last five words are nonsense words, but that they can be sounded out.

5. On the Student Record Sheet, mark each word correct (C) or incorrect (X) as the student reads down List #1.

6. Allow five seconds for each word. If a word has not been read correctly in five seconds, mark the word incorrect (X) and have the student continue reading.

7. Count and record the total number of errors at the bottom of List #1. If five or more words are incorrect in List #1, stop testing. If fewer than five words are incorrect, continue with List #2, and so on. Stop testing if a child makes five or more errors on any list.

8. Use the Level 1 Placement Chart to see where review or instruction should begin for that student.

9. Students who successfully complete all five word lists with fewer than five errors on each are ready for *Sing, Spell, Read & Write*® Level 2.

Sing, Spell, Read & Write®

Achievement Test #2

Student Record Sheet

Student _____

Examiner _____

Date _____ Grade _____ School _____

List #1

1. map
2. gas
3. has
4. net
5. pen
6. the
7. hid
8. tip
9. is
10. tot
11. job
12. from
13. jug
14. bud
15. lump

Nonsense Words:

16. hig
17. bod
18. laz
19. med
20. puz

Total Errors: _____

Five or more errors: Stop testing and see Quick Placement Chart on laminated Teacher Directions. Less than five errors: Continue with List #2.

List #2

1. who
2. once
3. very
4. neat
5. weep
6. leap
7. gain
8. note
9. rice
10. trace
11. shy
12. huge
13. lady
14. batter
15. sport
16. ship
17. chin
18. her
19. bird
20. curl

Total Errors: _____

Five or more errors: Stop testing and see Quick Placement Chart on laminated Teacher Directions. Less than five errors: Continue with List #3.

List #3

1. that
2. both
3. pitch
4. owl
5. out
6. own
7. few
8. quit
9. whale
10. star
11. saw
12. auto
13. ring
14. sang
15. long
16. toy
17. oil
18. hook
19. cool
20. nation

Total Errors: _____

Five or more errors: Stop testing and see Quick Placement Chart on laminated Teacher Directions. Less than five errors: Continue with List #4.

List #4

1. might
2. caught
3. enough
4. through
5. small
6. warm
7. hedge
8. due
9. wax
10. chief
11. steak
12. feather
13. earth
14. leaves
15. mind
16. cold
17. bushy
18. fair
19. juice
20. motor

Total Errors: _____

Five or more errors: Stop testing and see Quick Placement Chart on laminated Teacher Directions. Less than five errors: Continue with List #5.

List #5

1. didn't
2. care
3. wasp
4. prince
5. wrote
6. know
7. should
8. comb
9. sign
10. honest
11. listen
12. mosquitoes
13. Joseph
14. anchor
15. mission
16. friend
17. Charlotte
18. ocean
19. investigation
20. shoes

Total Errors: _____

Five or more errors: Stop testing and see Quick Placement Chart on laminated Teacher Directions. Less than five errors: Continue with List #1.

Achievement Test #2

List #1	List #2	List #3	List #4	List #5
1. map	1. who	1. that	1. might	1. didn't
2. gas	2. once	2. both	2. caught	2. care
3. has	3. very	3. pitch	3. enough	3. wasp
4. net	4. neat	4. owl	4. through	4. prince
5. pen	5. weep	5. out	5. small	5. wrote
6. the	6. leap	6. own	6. warm	6. know
7. hid	7. gain	7. few	7. hedge	7. should
8. tip	8. note	8. quit	8. due	8. comb
9. is	9. rice	9. whale	9. wax	9. sign
10. tot	10. trace	10. star	10. chief	10. honest
11. job	11. shy	11. saw	11. steak	11. listen
12. from	12. huge	12. auto	12. feather	12. mosquitoes
13. jug	13. lady	13. ring	13. earth	13. Joseph
14. bud	14. batter	14. sang	14. leaves	14. anchor
15. lump	15. sport	15. long	15. mind	15. mission
16. hig	16. ship	16. toy	16. cold	16. friend
17. bod	17. chin	17. oil	17. bushy	17. Charlotte
18. laz	18. her	18. hook	18. fair	18. ocean
19. med	19. bird	19. cool	19. juice	19. investigation
20. puz	20. curl	20. nation	20. motor	20. shoes

Level 1 Placement Chart

	Level 1 Begin with: **Raceway Step**	Phonetic Skills Student needs instruction in:	Correlated Songs & Charts Have students sing and do these activities:	Correlated Games Have students play these games:
Five or more errors on **List #1:**	1	Short Vowel Words	*A to Z Phonics Song* and Wall Cards ABC Echoes and Manuscript Wall Chart *Short Vowel Song* and Cards *Ferris Wheel Song,* Chart, and Tickets Short Vowel Word Charts (5)	A to Z Sound-O A to Z Pick-A-Sound
Five or more errors on **List #2:**	16	Letter Clusters Long Vowels Two-Vowel Words Silent ¢ Words	*Letter Cluster Phonics Song* and Charts (4) Pop the Balloons Chart *Long Vowel Marching Song* and Cards *Two Vowels Get Together Song,* Chart, and Word Cards *Silent ¢ Song,* Chart, and Word Cards	Letter Cluster Sound-O Letter Cluster Pick-A-Sound Word-O
Five or more errors on **List #3:**	23	Letter Clusters (continued)	(same as previous box)	
Five or more errors on **List #4:**	27	Oddities of the English Language	*Gh Clown Song* and Charts	
Five or more errors on **List #5:**	30	Contractions Silent Letters Multisyllable Words Borrowers & Wacky Words		

Name _____   Date _____

Review Words for
Raceway Steps 8, 10, 12, and 14

Lists of short-vowel review words are provided on pp. 198–205. Each set of pages can provide additional practice in reading previously-learned short-vowel words before children take the corresponding Book End Assessment. You may wish to have children practice reading the words as a class, in small groups, in pairs, or independently.

• Pages 198–199: Short **a** and **e** words	Book End Assessment 2
• Pages 200–201: Short **a**, **e**, and **i** words	Book End Assessment 3
• Pages 202–203: Short **a**, **e**, **i**, and **o** words	Book End Assessment 4
• Pages 204–205: Short **a**, **e**, **i**, **o**, and **u** words	Book End Assessment 5

Sing, Spell, Read & Write

Short a, e Review Words

Name _____ Date _____

cat	ten	well
ham	Sam	egg
map	can	Max
Val	bed	yes
get	mat	tap
rag	cap	bed
pan	Hal	pass
leg	jam	has
Dad	jet	fan
bat	fat	pet
a	had	Dan
Nan	fed	sad
wet	hat	pen
and	fell	Jeff
tell	gas	red
as	hen	lap
Ken	man	end
bag	Peg	tag

less	yell	left
Pam	the	mend
bet	Sal	crab
van	tells	next
let	wax	glad
bad	neck	west
mess	yells	raft
ran	best	eggs
met	sent	rest
nap	fast	sand
pal	gets	help
yet	peck	scat
pat	belt	clap
tan	past	held
have	bent	grab
Tess	went	
wag	hand	
sat	last	

Short a, e, i Review Words

Name _____   Date _____

pig	can	had
van	wig	yet
tip	Jim	fill
bed	beg	him
kid	cat	lid
pen	fix	has
fit	Dad	Sis
mat	did	hen
dig	leg	hip
bat	Sam	fell
in	dip	hid
pin	Bill	Tim
it	end	hill
fed	lip	and
sip	map	sit
big	Liz	if
fat	wet	cap
bit	rim	is

ran	well	digs
Jill	win	nest
red	yell	gets
lit	the	sent
miss	yip	help
his	mitt	left
Ken	wins	bent
six	have	milk
zip	mess	mend
less	tips	lift
will	Ripp	slip
as	back	clap
pass	give	grins
rat	went	quick
rip	spin	can't
hit	past	
ten	eggs	
kiss	fast	

Short a, e, i, o Review Words

Name _____ Date _____

job	dip	his
ox	got	Mom
will	fog	end
hot	red	Dot
pop	fit	is
big	Bob	hog
cot	in	as
box	log	lot
hid	wet	doll
Don	fox	kiss
cat	Rob	rod
hop	zip	wag
Kim	has	Tom
cob	mop	less
jog	pass	pig
gas	rot	pot
top	bed	Sis
pen	not	yet

sob	sand	stop
on	lock	milk
ten	nest	help
set	sock	still
to	past	frog
nod	left	Spot
yell	Kim's	crab
have	was	glad
Todd	dock	plop
mess	fast	grins
digs	give	socks
odd	went	clap
miss	gets	from
said	dots	blocks
the	Jill's	pom-pom
ask	pond	
rock	spin	
belt	mend	

Short a, e, i, o, u Review Words

Name _____   Date _____

up	cut	gum
mud	rub	Gus
hug	Dad	has
as	dull	him
bed	bug	his
cup	hut	hit
bud	fun	hot
dug	pup	top
bus	Tim	hum
ten	pig	Sam
but	tub	tug
in	log	us
ran	nut	ask
pot	sip	buzz
mug	Mom	cups
tap	rug	is
wet	bun	on
hop	rob	run

not	less	plop
fuss	milk	the
pal	duck	snug
fuzz	must	give
dust	of	to
have	miss	still
Mutt	pump	dress
will	help	glass
puff	rubs	truck
Judd	said	drip
pet	past	stuck
jump	step	rub-a-dub-dub
Tom	dump	was
just	swim	um•brel•la
kick	gulp	
left	stop	
sun	drum	
rust	from	

Name:

School:

Grade:

Date:

*This is to certify that
the student named above
has completed the
Level 1 Program of*

Sing, Spell,
Read & Write®

Teacher:

Principal:

Winner